WORD SEARCH®

Over 200 puzzles

D0301083

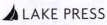 LAKE PRESS

Lake Press Pty Ltd
5 Burwood Road
Hawthorn VIC 3122 Australia
www.lakepress.com.au

First published 2019
Printed in China 5 4 3 2
LP19 524

R	A	T	L	A	R	B	I	G	E	N	I	I	L	B
M	N	I	N	D	O	N	E	S	I	A	A	I	T	I
I	I	C	H	A	D	C	T	L	B	B	T	Y	U	R
R	N	I	U	A	E	O	I	O	A	H	I	A	R	S
E	E	A	U	E	N	T	L	L	U	R	E	K	K	M
L	B	L	R	I	A	I	R	A	G	L	U	B	E	A
A	N	G	A	L	V	R	N	Q	I	E	Q	S	Y	N
N	O	E	Y	I	H	I	A	M	L	R	I	A	A	T
D	O	R	A	S	A	D	N	A	M	I	B	I	A	E
A	R	I	A	S	A	A	G	I	Y	M	M	D	A	I
I	E	A	A	N	R	U	S	E	A	E	A	O	A	V
B	M	I	A	I	T	P	Y	N	N	X	Z	B	A	I
M	A	C	J	R	A	L	R	U	M	I	O	M	B	I
A	C	A	O	I	N	A	I	R	A	C	M	A	U	D
Z	H	P	N	B	F	I	A	B	R	O	P	C	C	L

COUNTRIES

ALGERIA
BELARUS
BENIN
BOLIVIA
BRUNEI
BULGARIA
CAMBODIA
CAMEROON
CANADA
CHAD

CUBA
ESTONIA
FIJI
GIBRALTAR
GREECE
INDONESIA
IRAN
IRELAND
ITALY
LITHUANIA

MEXICO
MOZAMBIQUE
MYANMAR
NAMIBIA
PORTUGAL
SPAIN
SYRIA
TURKEY
VIETNAM
ZAMBIA

Y	L	B	B	T	N	O	O	C	E	N	I	A	M	D
O	I	I	L	O	N	I	K	H	C	N	U	M	I	W
R	A	R	A	Y	B	U	R	M	I	L	L	A	O	E
N	T	M	C	G	X	T	N	B	I	X	X	R	E	L
K	B	A	K	E	A	N	O	R	U	L	E	B	C	F
D	O	N	A	R	B	M	Y	E	R	G	R	U	N	N
E	B	N	O	C	B	A	R	H	O	E	H	R	A	O
V	E	K	A	A	L	T	M	N	P	D	S	M	I	E
O	S	C	Y	I	R	A	R	B	O	S	I	E	N	L
N	E	E	Y	A	S	E	P	N	I	N	N	S	I	O
R	N	P	H	M	X	R	S	E	S	N	R	E	S	P
E	A	C	X	J	R	K	E	K	R	A	O	C	S	A
X	P	N	B	P	O	I	I	P	I	M	C	E	Y	N
T	A	A	B	Y	U	N	C	L	A	G	N	E	B	G
M	J	E	I	S	U	A	H	C	E	Y	B	B	A	T

BREEDS OF CAT

ABYSSINIAN
BAMBINO
BENGAL
BIRMAN
BLACK
BOMBAY
BURMESE
BURMILLA
CHARTREUX
CHAUSIE

CORNISH REX
CYMRIC
DEVON REX
DONSKOY
DWELF
JAPANESE BOBTAIL
KORAT
LAPERM
MAINE COON
MANX

MINSKIN
MUNCHKIN
NAPOLEON
OREGON REX
PERSIAN
SPHYNX
TABBY
TOYGER

TYPES OF SHRUB

```
R M U N R U B I V L A U R E L
A I E L D D U B Y B R O O M I
A A Z A L E A N L M A L L O W
A A N C A B O W I S T E R I A
E C A D N E Y Y R G C A L I L
G L E S P V L S D O G W O O D
N E A H I L E M U N R U B A L
A M R U O B J H E A T H E R A
R A I H E A C I N O P A J F V
D T P H S M A G N O L I A U E
Y I S M F O R S Y T H I A C N
H S I E G N A R O K C O M H D
E N A G N H A S O M I M S S E
E L N R O H T E R I F A E I R
R S U M Y N O U E E N H P A D
```

AZALEA	HEATHER	LILAC
BROOM	HEBE	MAGNOLIA
BUDDLEIA	HOLLY	MALLOW
CLEMATIS	HYDRANGEA	MIMOSA
DAPHNE	IVY	MOCK ORANGE
DOGWOOD	JAPONICA	PEONY
EUONYMUS	JASMINE	SPIRAEA
FIRETHORN	LABURNUM	VIBURNUM
FORSYTHIA	LAUREL	WISTERIA
FUCHSIA	LAVENDER	

R	E	H	C	S	N	I	P	E	E	S	R	D	G	R
G	S	B	U	N	A	I	N	A	R	E	M	O	P	V
O	P	E	E	Y	N	A	E	F	V	T	G	U	P	O
D	I	A	D	O	D	E	F	E	N	T	P	S	P	T
L	T	G	R	T	I	I	I	L	B	E	P	B	D	I
L	Z	L	A	L	T	R	L	A	B	R	A	D	O	R
U	N	E	L	S	T	G	R	E	Y	H	O	U	N	D
B	R	O	A	E	D	T	E	R	R	I	E	R	N	Y
G	C	M	R	G	O	D	P	E	E	H	S	A	E	K
R	D	A	C	H	S	H	U	N	D	T	H	G	R	S
R	C	H	I	H	U	A	H	U	A	G	N	A	E	U
D	A	L	M	A	T	I	A	N	F	E	U	I	X	H
C	O	C	K	E	R	S	P	A	N	I	E	L	O	F
F	D	A	G	L	D	N	U	O	H	X	O	F	B	P
O	N	O	A	R	K	E	L	P	I	E	N	H	R	D

BREEDS OF DOG

AFGHAN
BEAGLE
BOXER
BULLDOG
CHIHUAHUA
COCKER SPANIEL
COLLIE
DACHSHUND
DALMATIAN

FOXHOUND
GREAT DANE
GREYHOUND
HUSKY
KELPIE
LABRADOR
MASTIFF
PINSCHER
POINTER

POMERANIAN
PUG
RETRIEVER
SETTER
SHEEPDOG
SPITZ
TERRIER

4

```
R L E C N A C S I L E N C E R
E R A C U P U T A N E N D T O
S H D S O T O I H M E S T O P
T O L U S N T F U R W D E S H
R L O B S R C L H E O N I C R
A D H M E O T E O U I T O L S
I B H E R S E I A Q S K T M E
N A T R P N C L B L P H O L L
M C I G E E R O L I B T U I E
T K W E R C P L O E H U U P L
T U O P M A T S C E U N R R T
T U O K C O L B R A N Q I N L
S Q U A S H E L G N A R T S N
C P H S U R C D U C C H O K E
T U E C K E E P I N C H E C K
```

PUT A STOP TO IT

BLOCK OUT
CANCEL
CENSOR
CHOKE
CONCEAL
CRUSH
ELIDE
HOLD BACK
HUSH UP

INHIBIT
KEEP IN CHECK
PUT AN END TO
QUELL
REPRESS
RESTRAIN
SILENCE
SMOTHER
SQUASH

STAMP OUT
STIFLE
STOP
STRANGLE
SUBMERGE
THROTTLE
WITHHOLD

R	I	M	H	C	M	H	Y	A	N	I	R	A	S	T
P	N	P	E	R	U	P	S	O	R	A	S	E	A	C
R	M	O	A	O	G	H	R	R	R	K	R	R	E	P
M	A	A	D	R	E	A	K	I	H	E	A	I	O	O
A	H	A	O	E	B	R	I	A	N	E	C	T	M	R
H	A	G	F	P	D	A	N	H	C	C	E	I	E	E
A	R	A	S	M	U	O	G	O	A	N	E	D	V	G
R	A	P	T	E	C	H	N	L	T	H	A	S	U	E
A	J	N	A	R	E	S	I	A	K	E	S	E	S	N
N	A	E	T	D	U	P	T	K	L	I	L	P	N	T
I	H	K	E	L	H	E	E	A	S	H	O	G	U	N
L	A	R	E	N	E	G	R	O	N	R	E	V	O	G
N	N	G	I	E	R	E	V	O	S	N	I	Z	A	M
N	I	M	I	K	A	D	O	B	A	W	A	N	N	A
A	N	A	T	L	U	S	H	C	Q	U	E	E	N	A

ROYALS AND RULERS

AGA	KAISER	POTENTATE
BEGUM	KHAN	PRINCESS
CAESAR	KING	QUEEN
CALIPH	LEADER	REGENT
CONSUL	MAHARAJAH	SHAH
DUCE	MAHARANI	SHOGUN
EMIR	MIKADO	SOVEREIGN
EMPEROR	NAWAB	SULTANA
GOVERNOR-GENERAL	NIZAM	TSARINA
HEAD OF STATE	PHARAOH	VICEROY

MONGOL EMPERORS

ARIQ BOKE
AYURBARWADA
BERKE
JANI BEG
MENGU-TIMUR
OGEDEI KHAN
OGHUL QAIMISH

RINCHINBAL
SARTAQ
SHIDEBALA
TALABUGA
TEMUR KHAN
TINI BEG
TOQTA

TOREGENE KHATUN
TUDA MENGU
TUGH TEMUR
ULAGHCHI
URUS KHAN
UZBEG KHAN
YESUN TEMUR

T	E	C	N	A	L	A	B	P	A	Y	M	E	N	T
R	M	P	K	A	H	S	A	C	S	N	C	P	S	S
I	H	C	N	S	E	T	O	N	S	I	B	O	C	B
A	S	H	A	R	I	N	G	A	G	A	U	C	H	P
L	C	I	B	E	S	I	L	P	N	G	D	K	A	R
L	P	N	Y	S	I	E	S	P	I	R	G	E	N	O
O	L	T	G	A	P	Y	R	W	V	A	E	T	G	F
W	I	E	G	H	P	E	T	R	A	B	T	M	E	I
A	I	R	I	C	E	E	N	P	S	L	O	O	G	T
N	C	E	P	R	N	G	A	D	I	C	L	N	A	M
C	E	S	R	U	P	N	C	R	I	E	T	E	N	E
E	G	T	T	P	Y	O	E	P	N	N	C	Y	T	C
F	E	L	A	N	I	E	T	L	C	I	G	E	D	H
N	E	B	A	N	K	A	C	C	O	U	N	T	R	U
U	D	R	S	G	N	I	T	A	N	O	D	G	O	S

MANAGING MONEY

ALLOWANCE
BALANCE
BANK ACCOUNT
BARGAIN
BUDGET
CASH
CHANGE
COINS

DONATING
EARNING
INTEREST
NOTES
PAYMENT
PIGGY BANK
POCKET MONEY
PROFIT

PURCHASE
PURSE
RECEIPT
SALE
SAVING
SHARING
SPENDING
WALLET

P	I	L	O	T	U	L	O	B	N	W	H	I	T	E
B	L	A	C	K	F	I	S	H	C	C	U	D	E	H
B	O	T	T	L	E	N	O	S	E	O	C	A	N	I
K	N	E	E	L	A	B	A	L	T	K	H	A	E	H
H	A	G	U	L	E	B	I	D	I	P	R	S	U	D
U	L	B	R	N	E	B	O	L	U	W	C	M	E	E
N	E	H	T	I	B	L	L	L	H	D	P	H	S	D
M	R	H	I	A	G	E	I	A	E	B	T	C	O	H
C	D	L	Y	O	R	H	L	I	A	O	T	R	E	E
C	A	C	H	A	L	O	T	C	O	P	A	U	E	E
O	E	B	A	E	O	I	K	T	H	D	L	R	A	B
O	H	M	I	N	K	E	N	K	O	B	N	E	L	A
W	W	C	C	E	S	I	O	P	R	O	P	O	C	C
Y	O	O	D	N	A	L	N	E	E	R	G	R	T	A
B	B	B	S	U	P	M	A	R	G	O	O	R	A	A

WHALES AND DOLPHINS

BALEEN	DORADO	PILOT
BAY	GRAMPUS	PORPOISE
BELUGA	GREENLAND	RIGHT
BLACKFISH	HUMPBACK	SEI
BLUE	KILLER	TOOTHED
BOTTLENOSE	MINKE	WHITE
BOWHEAD	NARWHAL	
CACHALOT	ORCA	

P	O	O	G	D	O	G	E	N	E	S	I	S	O	N
T	D	R	A	D	Y	E	N	I	G	N	E	C	P	O
X	N	T	M	Y	D	O	G	G	B	I	V	I	G	I
T	E	D	E	Y	O	F	R	O	Y	V	I	G	G	T
U	T	T	G	F	G	B	I	N	E	I	T	A	A	A
R	N	S	E	N	A	S	L	B	J	N	A	M	M	T
B	I	A	A	U	D	G	C	A	A	W	X	E	E	S
O	N	C	R	A	A	S	G	D	U	B	N	B	C	Y
G	R	M	E	Y	H	U	V	N	O	T	U	O	U	A
R	E	A	A	T	A	A	U	X	B	C	R	Y	B	L
A	P	E	S	R	N	O	M	W	I	I	U	I	E	P
F	U	R	N	C	N	C	E	E	G	A	G	N	V	G
X	S	D	E	I	Y	E	E	L	Y	N	X	U	G	G
T	F	O	S	O	R	C	I	M	R	E	X	R	C	O
U	N	T	H	C	T	I	W	S	I	N	C	E	R	X

GAMES CONSOLES

ADVANCE	JAGUAR	SUPER NINTENDO
DREAMCAST	LYNX	SWITCH
DSI	MICROSOFT	TURBOGRAFX
GAME BOY	NEO GEO	VIRTUAL BOY
GAMECUBE	N-GAGE	VITA
GAME GEAR	PC ENGINE	WII U
GENESIS	PLAYSTATION	XBOX

GRAPES

ALIGOTE
BARBERA
CATAWBA
CONCORD
DELAWARE
FURMINT
GAMAY
HARSLEVELU
MALBEC

MALMSEY
MALVASIA
NEBBIOLO
PINOTAGE
PINOT BLANC
RULANDER
SAUVIGNON
SCHEUREBE
SEMILLON

SERCIAL
SEYVAL BLANC
SHIRAZ
SILVANER
STEEN
SYRAH
TREBBIANO
VERDELHO

U	L	I	R	Q	U	I	Z	Z	I	C	A	L	G	Y
T	R	D	E	L	Z	Z	U	P	P	Z	A	U	I	Z
Z	G	A	I	J	E	N	I	N	A	Z	Z	E	M	Z
L	N	Z	Z	A	A	I	F	I	Z	Z	E	D	A	U
G	I	P	Z	Z	N	G	N	I	L	Z	Z	U	N	F
R	Z	G	A	Z	M	Z	N	I	U	Z	D	S	S	R
I	Z	I	N	Y	L	A	N	I	S	R	R	I	E	E
Z	U	Z	S	I	I	G	T	Y	Z	Y	A	Z	L	I
Z	B	L	I	A	Z	Z	J	A	Z	I	Z	Z	Z	Z
L	N	P	A	H	Z	Z	Z	Z	Z	Z	L	Z	Z	
I	Z	E	I	A	W	Z	I	U	H	Z	I	E	U	I
E	A	P	Z	A	Z	T	I	U	C	B	L	D	M	R
R	L	I	I	P	Z	A	Z	P	Q	A	B	Z	N	F
I	P	G	N	I	L	Z	Z	U	P	Z	J	Z	U	U
M	E	Z	Z	O	A	P	A	P	A	R	A	Z	Z	I

DOUBLE-Z WORDS

BLIZZARD	JAZZY	PUZZLING
BUZZING	MEZZANINE	QUIZZICAL
DIZZY	MEZZO	QUIZZING
FIZZED	MUZZLES	RAZZMATAZZ
FRIZZIER	NUZZLING	SIZZLED
FUZZY	PAPARAZZI	SNAZZIER
GRIZZLIER	PIAZZA	TIZZY
GUZZLING	PIZAZZ	UNMUZZLE
HUZZA	PIZZA	WHIZZ
JACUZZI	PUZZLED	ZIZZ

A	N	E	A	T	E	N	E	F	L	U	F	F	N	C
K	G	E	W	E	K	D	H	S	P	A	O	S	A	F
M	P	O	M	E	E	C	R	S	N	S	E	E	E	P
P	A	P	T	T	N	E	I	A	U	I	E	N	L	W
E	T	K	C	T	E	E	T	P	E	R	R	A	C	I
Y	P	Y	E	S	F	N	K	A	T	L	B	R	Y	P
C	U	D	F	S	W	L	I	I	G	R	C	E	R	E
O	E	I	N	E	P	A	O	F	L	I	S	D	D	U
M	C	T	I	N	D	O	B	S	E	E	M	N	P	L
B	U	S	S	I	A	W	T	H	S	R	K	U	R	S
S	R	S	I	H	F	H	S	L	I	S	I	A	F	E
E	P	W	D	S	C	I	E	A	E	E	O	L	M	G
U	S	I	A	B	L	E	A	C	H	S	R	A	A	R
C	T	L	I	O	R	E	T	L	I	F	S	S	K	U
A	C	L	P	S	E	B	E	M	U	U	C	A	V	P

MAKING IT CLEAN

BLEACH
BRUSH
CLEAR
COMB
DISINFECT
DRY-CLEAN
EMPTY
FILTER
FLOSS
FLUFF

FUMIGATE
LAUNDER
MAKE LIKE NEW
MAKE SPOTLESS
MOP
NEATEN
PICK
POLISH
PURGE
REFINE

RINSE
SHINE
SOAK
SOAP
SPRUCE UP
SWAB
SWILL
TIDY
VACUUM
WIPE

TYPES OF PASTA

CANNELLONI
FARFALLE
FIORI
GEMELLI
GIGLI
GOMITI
LANTERNE
LASAGNE
LINGUINE

MANICOTTI
PENNE
RAVIOLI
RIGATONI
ROTELLE
ROTINI
SAGNARELLI
SPAGHETTI
SPIRALI

STROZZAPRETI
TAGLIATELLE
TORTELLINI
TORTIGLIONI
TRENETTE
TRENNE
TRIPOLINE
VERMICELLI
ZITI

```
A A I E O P O C A M R A H P A
C E T I E C A M A I E U O U I
G O A M Y T H O P O E I A P E
R A D I O A U T O G R A P H O
E A R O O I A D U B E P N M P
C O N E T U E A E O Z L A U O
R A E A I U Q I L E R A I B P
U M I E O O R E N A M T S E O
O I A A C A O O S G E E U A S
A L I I U E M G N A Q A O U O
I M I O E G I I A U T U I I R
G E A U E U U O I E A E O S P
E S E M U E T O O P E D M H E
I A U I U A U I L L A A O T A
Q N S Q E S R H C E E U H U G
```

4+ CONSECUTIVE VOWEL WORDS

BEAUISH	MAIEUTIC	PROSOPOPOEIA
CAMAIEU	METASEQUOIA	QUEUING
GIAOUR	MIAOUED	RADIOAUTOGRAPH
GOOIER	MYTHOPOEIA	RELIQUIAE
GUAIAC	OBSEQUIOUS	SAOUARI
HOMOIOUSIAN	PHARMACOPOEIA	ZOEAE
LOOIE	PLATEAUED	

A	I	E	H	P	O	R	T	S	O	P	A	N	T	E
S	H	T	R	O	P	E	S	E	H	L	R	E	U	T
C	E	A	H	M	H	Y	T	E	L	O	C	P	P	T
A	X	I	N	T	N	R	R	I	H	N	H	E	E	A
N	A	H	I	T	O	O	T	P	A	O	N	T	I	T
S	M	P	A	C	I	E	A	N	N	T	R	E	A	E
I	E	X	H	C	R	T	O	Y	A	A	O	A	C	E
O	T	E	I	A	E	S	H	M	M	P	S	N	L	U
N	E	E	T	M	N	S	E	E	O	I	A	I	C	P
C	R	I	R	O	P	T	T	T	S	N	S	S	A	H
S	O	E	C	O	E	E	A	O	O	I	M	I	E	E
N	C	R	N	R	R	M	I	S	O	R	S	M	S	M
P	E	D	E	E	O	E	S	N	H	E	N	I	U	I
A	E	O	I	N	M	A	Z	N	A	T	S	L	R	S
E	O	I	O	H	Y	P	E	R	B	O	L	E	A	M

LITERARY TERMS

ALLITERATION
ANTITHESIS
APOSTROPHE
ASSONANCE
CAESURA
CONSONANCE
ELISION
EPITHET
EUPHEMISM

EUPHONY
HEROIC
HEXAMETER
HYPERBOLE
MEIOSIS
METAPHOR
ONOMATOPOEIA
PENTAMETER
SCANSION

SIMILE
SPONDEE
STANZA
SYNTAX
TETRAMETER
TROCHEE
TROPE

U	P	Y	A	R	U	B	I	L	A	C	X	E	T	B
P	A	O	O	Z	Z	A	L	A	P	S	S	R	O	A
N	A	I	T	E	N	E	V	C	H	T	O	A	I	L
F	L	A	M	I	N	G	O	A	R	P	M	Y	G	L
A	S	O	T	H	L	M	R	A	I	O	S	W	A	Y
L	U	X	O	R	I	R	T	C	A	I	T	Y	L	S
A	N	S	M	R	A	O	A	E	R	I	E	N	L	T
L	R	M	A	H	S	N	C	A	I	E	R	N	E	Y
L	I	G	L	P	A	A	P	R	E	X	R	A	B	C
O	E	A	H	M	O	N	T	E	C	A	R	L	O	R
I	L	E	I	M	A	N	D	A	L	A	Y	B	A	Y
R	R	U	S	U	C	R	I	C	S	U	C	R	I	C
E	C	A	L	A	P	S	R	A	S	E	A	C	A	E
T	H	E	C	O	S	M	O	P	O	L	I	T	A	N
A	N	E	W	Y	O	R	K	N	E	W	Y	O	R	K

VEGAS CASINOS

ARIA
BALLY'S
BELLAGIO
CAESARS PALACE
CIRCUS CIRCUS
EXCALIBUR
FLAMINGO

HARRAH'S
LUXOR
MANDALAY BAY
MIRAGE
MONTE CARLO
NEW YORK NEW YORK
PALAZZO

PARIS
RIO
STRATOSPHERE
THE COSMOPOLITAN
TROPICANA
VENETIAN
WYNN

L	R	G	U	R	E	I	P	A	R	E	M	S	A	E
G	A	L	E	R	A	S	T	H	E	L	E	N	S	A
R	I	I	N	I	R	O	T	N	A	S	Y	P	M	K
U	U	L	Y	A	T	A	A	L	E	I	M	I	M	N
L	U	A	O	E	T	N	A	V	R	H	A	N	A	A
A	N	O	P	B	R	L	U	A	S	E	U	A	M	R
W	O	T	F	E	M	V	G	N	R	K	N	T	O	I
U	S	A	U	I	H	O	U	N	T	L	A	U	N	G
N	D	K	J	A	N	U	R	L	O	A	L	B	T	A
C	U	A	I	G	Y	M	A	T	C	Y	O	O	S	R
T	H	R	O	T	E	I	D	E	S	A	A	R	E	U
S	A	K	U	R	A	J	I	M	A	M	N	M	R	M
A	E	U	A	L	I	K	U	N	Z	E	N	O	R	A
A	S	U	I	V	U	S	E	V	H	I	A	V	A	Y
Y	O	K	S	V	E	H	C	U	Y	L	K	L	T	N

VOLCANOES

ETNA
FUJI
GALERAS
HEKLA
HUDSON
KILAUEA
KLYUCHEVSKOY
KRAKATOA
MAUNA LOA

MAYON
MERAPI
MONTSERRAT
NYAMURAGIRA
NYIRAGONGO
PINATUBO
RUAPEHU
SAKURAJIMA
SANTORINI

ST HELENS
STROMBOLI
TAAL
TEIDE
ULAWUN
UNZEN
VESUVIUS
VULCANO

L	C	P	A	C	E	B	N	R	T	E	R	C	A	M
M	E	N	I	A	M	Q	A	O	Y	O	V	L	P	A
C	P	T	N	N	T	M	U	R	L	E	L	L	T	E
P	A	S	C	A	L	O	M	A	R	L	S	A	M	R
E	N	T	E	S	L	A	O	M	R	E	A	O	R	M
J	O	U	L	E	E	D	O	F	M	T	L	G	T	E
N	L	I	I	M	L	T	R	P	S	E	B	C	K	N
O	E	H	B	A	O	M	A	A	P	H	K	E	O	A
R	H	E	C	T	P	A	D	R	Y	C	L	C	R	P
E	S	A	E	I	M	R	I	O	A	V	P	P	E	S
A	U	S	L	B	L	D	M	B	I	C	I	I	O	P
P	B	R	I	U	L	A	R	N	R	E	T	N	N	R
I	O	F	M	C	B	C	E	N	I	A	H	C	C	T
D	P	M	T	M	S	A	F	A	T	H	O	M	A	H
E	C	E	S	R	A	P	I	T	H	E	R	M	C	A

UNITS OF MEASUREMENT

ACRE
ARE
BARREL
BUSHEL
CARAT
CHAIN
CUBIT
DRAM
FATHOM
FERMI

FOOT
GALLON
INCH
JOULE
KELVIN
MILE
MOLE
PACE
PARSEC
PASCAL

PECK
PINT
POLE
QUART
REAM
ROD
SPAN
TESLA
THERM
YARD

L	H	S	N	I	T	R	U	C	E	H	G	G	M	F
Y	K	T	G	M	E	C	U	R	B	U	N	D	C	A
O	S	C	U	L	L	I	N	L	F	G	I	R	E	D
N	N	L	F	S	N	P	R	B	O	H	T	A	W	D
S	W	P	T	L	O	H	A	O	R	E	A	L	E	E
N	I	K	A	E	D	S	E	G	D	S	E	L	N	N
Y	K	I	R	C	F	I	S	H	E	R	K	I	M	O
E	O	E	A	N	O	T	R	O	G	T	A	G	E	T
L	O	I	K	A	F	O	F	D	O	D	W	H	N	R
F	C	C	I	W	N	R	R	A	T	A	K	C	Z	A
I	D	W	E	I	A	A	T	N	T	T	A	C	I	B
H	D	I	R	S	W	H	D	S	E	I	O	G	E	U
C	W	U	E	O	W	D	O	E	A	H	K	B	S	T
W	D	R	H	R	K	N	O	H	A	M	C	M	B	O
D	L	I	A	D	M	A	L	T	I	H	W	A	M	A

AUSTRALIAN PRIME MINISTERS

ABBOTT	FRASER	MCMAHON
BARTON	GILLARD	MENZIES
BRUCE	GORTON	PAGE
CHIFLEY	HAWKE	REID
COOK	HOLT	RUDD
CURTIN	HOWARD	SCULLIN
DEAKIN	HUGHES	WATSON
FADDEN	KEATING	WHITLAM
FISHER	LYONS	
FORDE	MCEWEN	

```
A N N M D E K A M E K A M K E
U E A N A S M I L K Y W A Y T
S P T S D U O L C T R O O T I
O T I E A N N S I R E A Y E L
L U T R E E S U M T R O A N L
A N E E T V P E S B L R W A E
R E U C N K U I P E R B E L T
W A E N N A S K E R H I Y P A
I L S O E I L R P L U T O F S
N C O T A A S P U S U N A R U
D M N I E P R A R A T A O A L
M E R C U R Y T T O T E N W O
O R R E I N O E H U N N M D M
S R A M J U P I T E R I E O S
I A E M U A H E D U R N M C C
```

THE SOLAR SYSTEM

ASTEROID
CENTAURS
CERES
COMET
DWARF PLANET
EARTH
ERIS
HAUMEA
JUPITER

KUIPER BELT
MAKEMAKE
MARS
MERCURY
MILKY WAY
MINOR PLANET
MOON
NEPTUNE
OORT CLOUD

ORBIT
PLUTO
SATELLITE
SATURN
SOLAR WIND
THE SUN
TITAN
URANUS
VENUS

S	E	N	L	O	U	S	E	E	T	L	O	S	G	O
P	Q	H	B	B	S	C	E	E	O	A	G	R	S	C
I	I	U	E	E	M	A	R	B	C	R	A	B	U	T
M	T	I	I	R	E	M	S	R	R	S	U	U	S	O
I	C	O	O	D	I	T	I	S	S	T	A	C	C	P
L	E	W	M	T	E	C	L	H	T	L	O	O	E	U
L	S	B	E	R	K	U	O	E	U	R	C	C	D	S
I	N	O	U	E	G	P	R	T	P	K	D	I	E	M
P	I	S	T	O	P	F	N	I	R	U	D	C	P	R
E	K	N	L	E	L	A	O	O	G	S	D	A	I	E
D	C	A	R	Y	R	N	A	W	C	U	I	D	T	D
E	I	I	I	A	T	C	A	I	U	O	B	A	N	I
A	T	L	T	O	H	S	T	H	T	S	R	O	E	P
N	S	M	T	T	P	A	P	H	I	D	C	A	C	S
E	L	E	E	C	H	E	H	S	H	T	O	M	L	L

INVERTEBRATES

APHID	CRICKET	SLUG
BEETLE	GRASSHOPPER	SNAIL
BUG	LEECH	SPIDER
BUTTERFLY	LOBSTER	SQUID
CENTIPEDE	LOUSE	STICK INSECT
CICADA	MILLIPEDE	TARANTULA
COCKROACH	MOTH	TERMITE
CORAL	OCTOPUS	WASP
CRAB	SCORPION	WORM

D	O	D	V	D	P	L	A	Y	E	R	I	O	O	L
O	R	E	H	S	A	W	H	S	I	D	M	H	U	W
R	E	K	A	M	H	C	I	W	D	N	A	S	R	N
E	H	H	B	R	E	D	N	E	L	B	M	E	E	R
E	E	U	L	L	A	P	T	O	P	C	N	V	E	N
R	A	M	O	D	U	C	H	C	T	A	O	K	E	O
E	T	I	I	A	A	R	O	O	E	D	A	L	L	I
K	E	D	D	N	R	M	A	L	R	M	U	P	L	S
O	R	I	A	A	P	S	C	Y	E	N	F	E	I	I
O	E	F	R	U	T	M	S	E	P	H	O	D	R	V
C	E	I	T	E	U	I	F	A	K	L	L	R	G	E
W	W	E	R	U	A	F	Y	I	E	A	A	R	I	L
O	R	R	C	C	O	N	S	O	L	E	R	Y	G	E
L	M	A	D	C	T	E	L	E	P	H	O	N	E	T
S	V	E	V	A	W	O	R	C	I	M	O	U	D	R

HOUSEHOLD APPLIANCES

BLENDER	GRILL	RADIO
BLU-RAY PLAYER	HEATER	SANDWICH MAKER
COFFEE MAKER	HUMIDIFIER	SLOW COOKER
COMPUTER	IRON	TELEPHONE
CONSOLE	LAPTOP	TELEVISION
DISHWASHER	MICROWAVE	TOASTER
DVD PLAYER	OVEN	VACUUM CLEANER

C	A	N	A	D	A	I	D	O	B	M	A	C	S	L
N	L	P	S	T	A	G	N	O	T	U	I	V	D	A
U	Y	A	E	I	T	A	N	B	E	L	A	I	N	K
L	A	S	O	R	N	H	I	E	H	U	N	E	A	N
A	U	E	O	S	U	G	A	S	P	U	I	T	L	A
V	I	V	N	S	N	L	A	I	Y	A	T	N	S	L
U	E	I	R	I	O	I	P	P	L	A	L	A	I	I
T	N	D	U	A	U	U	A	A	O	A	L	M	N	R
A	U	L	P	R	F	G	T	E	L	R	N	A	O	S
O	R	A	O	E	U	I	W	H	L	A	E	D	M	P
M	B	M	A	I	K	A	J	E	K	E	U	E	O	A
A	A	I	S	S	U	R	N	I	N	O	L	U	L	P
S	A	I	L	O	G	N	O	M	T	I	R	S	O	U
A	I	D	N	I	S	A	N	I	H	C	N	E	S	A
C	V	A	N	U	A	T	U	C	P	I	E	D	A	L

ASIA-PACIFIC COUNTRIES

BHUTAN
BRUNEI
CAMBODIA
CANADA
CHILE
CHINA
FIJI
INDIA
LAOS
MALAYSIA

MALDIVES
MONGOLIA
NAURU
NEPAL
NEW GUINEA
NIUE
PALAU
PAPUA
PERU
RUSSIA

SAMOA
SINGAPORE
SOLOMON ISLANDS
SOUTH KOREA
SRI LANKA
THAILAND
TONGA
TUVALU
VANUATU
VIETNAM

T	L	C	I	T	S	I	L	A	E	R	N	U	I	I
O	S	U	I	K	O	S	S	I	L	L	Y	L	N	W
P	U	I	D	U	Y	F	E	T	U	S	L	A	B	R
K	O	C	D	I	O	T	E	L	U	I	T	C	A	I
C	R	O	I	O	C	S	T	O	E	F	C	I	T	M
A	E	K	L	T	I	R	L	A	A	S	L	S	L	P
R	T	I	E	W	O	U	O	D	B	U	N	N	R	R
C	S	N	N	S	C	I	O	U	C	I	D	E	I	U
H	O	U	O	I	D	E	D	E	S	T	O	S	S	D
I	P	O	D	U	R	C	P	I	D	E	O	N	R	E
R	E	I	P	I	A	S	T	U	P	I	D	O	S	N
A	R	O	U	T	R	A	G	E	O	U	S	N	S	T
R	P	I	M	P	R	A	C	T	I	C	A	B	L	E
T	A	B	S	U	R	D	E	K	A	B	F	L	A	H
U	E	L	B	I	S	N	O	P	S	E	R	R	I	I

A MAD IDEA

ABSURD
BATTY
CRACKPOT
DAFT
FOOLISH
HALF-BAKED
IDIOTIC

IMPRACTICABLE
IMPRUDENT
IRRESPONSIBLE
LUDICROUS
NONSENSICAL
OUTRAGEOUS
PECULIAR

PREPOSTEROUS
RIDICULOUS
SENSELESS
SILLY
STUPID
UNREALISTIC
UNWISE

B	A	P	T	I	S	T	E	R	Y	C	T	O	M	B
E	E	A	E	A	A	E	E	L	P	E	E	T	S	P
R	C	I	S	M	C	S	T	I	P	L	U	P	A	T
I	H	S	A	I	R	U	E	V	A	N	R	R	S	P
P	A	L	N	S	I	O	T	B	O	E	V	H	M	E
S	P	E	C	E	S	H	S	Y	S	I	R	Y	U	S
W	E	P	T	R	T	R	A	B	S	I	R	E	L	N
P	L	R	U	I	Y	E	Y	E	N	F	C	R	L	A
A	A	E	A	C	T	T	P	E	L	R	A	H	E	R
R	N	T	R	O	E	P	T	E	Y	D	T	C	C	T
C	I	S	Y	R	V	A	B	P	Y	L	N	L	A	T
L	C	I	Y	D	E	H	T	T	S	A	O	U	S	P
O	S	O	S	M	H	C	U	N	U	O	F	P	S	L
S	I	L	S	S	C	M	A	L	T	A	R	E	H	C
E	P	C	R	B	M	U	I	R	T	A	E	S	P	A

PARTS OF A CHURCH

ADYTUM
AISLE
ALTAR
APSE
ATRIUM
BAPTISTERY
BELFRY
CHAPEL
CHAPTER HOUSE
CHEVET

CLOISTER
CRYPT
FONT
MISERICORD
NAVE
PARCLOSE
PARVIS
PEW
PISCINA
PRESBYTERY

PULPIT
SACELLUM
SACRISTY
SANCTUARY
SEPULCHRE
SHRINE
SPIRE
STEEPLE
TOMB
TRANSEPT

T	T	L	T	S	A	L	T	C	E	L	L	A	R	T
T	S	S	T	A	R	B	O	X	T	B	P	D	E	R
T	N	R	E	T	N	A	L	F	A	E	R	F	S	A
W	L	I	C	N	E	P	L	L	T	I	R	O	A	D
E	A	T	S	E	L	O	L	A	B	W	T	R	B	I
P	O	H	Y	L	W	O	H	G	P	A	A	T	E	T
O	I	S	T	E	O	I	N	U	C	T	H	U	R	I
L	A	I	R	N	A	I	C	A	W	E	Y	N	A	O
E	B	F	B	R	P	W	T	S	E	R	T	E	U	N
V	S	A	U	P	A	A	E	N	C	B	R	T	Q	A
N	S	M	A	L	M	S	A	B	H	O	A	E	S	L
E	A	L	L	A	U	L	S	R	A	M	P	L	G	B
S	F	E	R	O	P	T	R	P	A	B	S	L	B	O
O	T	A	H	K	I	T	E	B	A	S	E	E	A	X
N	N	O	L	E	E	T	C	R	O	S	S	R	A	E

ORIGAMI MODELS

BALLOON BASE
CATAMARAN
CROSS
CUP
ENVELOPE
FISH
FLAPPING BIRD
FLOWER

FORTUNE TELLER
HOUSE
KITE BASE
LANTERN
PARTY HAT
PENCIL
PLANE
SALT CELLAR

SAMURAI HAT
SQUARE BASE
STAR BOX
TIE
TRADITIONAL BOX
WALLET
WATER BOMB

P	H	B	L	S	O	E	B	R	A	I	S	E	I	E
E	B	O	L	O	G	N	E	S	E	T	S	C	B	U
O	O	B	U	R	G	E	R	L	S	B	T	A	A	C
S	R	P	U	L	L	E	D	A	S	O	R	S	B	E
H	S	A	L	U	O	G	O	T	E	U	O	S	E	B
S	A	L	A	M	I	R	E	A	A	R	G	E	K	R
R	W	E	T	S	T	L	A	G	S	G	A	R	C	A
E	N	S	F	O	T	E	L	E	G	U	N	O	A	B
T	T	O	P	U	G	G	C	O	A	I	O	L	S	O
L	B	E	C	A	N	H	U	A	E	G	F	E	S	C
S	O	S	S	C	O	K	E	R	G	N	F	P	O	H
S	O	U	T	R	E	O	S	S	O	O	G	N	U	O
U	A	L	I	E	U	E	I	O	O	N	L	S	L	P
S	O	Z	M	E	A	T	B	A	L	L	L	A	E	S
E	O	G	T	O	N	K	O	W	U	E	A	O	T	B

MEAT DISHES

BARBECUE
BOLOGNESE
BOURGUIGNON
BRAISE
BURGER
CASSEROLE
CASSOULET

CHOPS
CHORIZO
CUTLETS
GOULASH
KEBAB
MEATBALL
POT ROAST

PULLED
SALAMI
SAUSAGE
STEAK
STEW
STROGANOFF

L	A	N	E	C	A	L	P	E	R	I	F	E	F	A
B	W	A	B	I	R	T	H	P	L	A	C	E	U	A
E	O	E	A	R	E	S	U	R	F	A	C	E	R	D
C	R	C	E	C	A	F	E	D	R	C	X	A	N	J
A	K	A	C	S	M	E	A	B	O	A	C	E	A	A
L	P	T	A	C	C	M	N	M	C	E	C	C	C	C
U	L	S	F	N	E	I	M	E	H	A	S	A	E	E
P	A	U	E	L	A	O	R	O	F	P	O	P	C	N
O	C	R	R	M	N	B	R	R	A	M	L	S	A	C
P	E	C	P	P	A	S	E	L	T	E	A	K	L	Y
C	A	R	L	T	E	T	A	A	E	C	C	K	R
L	A	A	E	E	N	C	E	K	C	B	E	A	C	R
E	C	M	A	I	E	M	B	R	A	C	E	B	E	U
E	P	A	C	E	D	E	N	O	T	E	C	A	N	P
S	H	O	E	L	A	C	E	C	A	M	I	R	G	C

"ACE" WORDS

ACETONE
ADJACENCY
BACKSPACE
BIRTHPLACE
COMMONPLACE
CRUSTACEAN
DEFACE
EMBRACE
EXACERBATE

FIREPLACE
FURNACE
GRIMACE
INTERFACE
MAINBRACE
NECKLACE
PACED
PALACE
PEACE

POPULACE
PREFACE
RACEHORSE
RESURFACE
SHOELACE
SOLACE
TACET
WORKPLACE

G	N	I	L	H	B	R	U	C	I	N	E	B	D	C
A	I	I	O	L	O	N	E	H	P	C	H	N	O	I
A	R	U	T	A	D	A	M	A	N	I	T	A	O	P
B	A	R	B	A	S	C	O	A	N	A	P	N	W	S
N	S	M	U	I	L	L	A	H	T	A	I	I	S	A
A	A	E	M	E	T	I	N	E	R	L	A	R	S	A
E	D	I	N	A	Y	C	R	S	L	E	O	I	A	N
A	T	I	M	B	O	A	I	A	A	N	D	N	S	O
N	N	M	E	I	R	N	H	E	T	I	I	O	B	B
I	I	O	B	U	E	P	A	I	U	I	O	E	E	E
P	R	A	C	E	R	G	O	T	C	N	X	R	N	H
O	D	I	B	E	B	O	E	A	I	O	I	E	Z	E
R	L	I	L	A	R	U	O	N	C	C	N	Z	E	N
T	A	I	Z	B	U	T	O	X	A	P	H	E	N	E
A	L	E	A	D	S	O	M	A	N	B	L	M	E	O

POISONS

ALDRIN
AMANITA
ARSINE
ASPIC
ATROPIN
BANE
BARBASCO
BENZENE
BRUCINE
CICUTA

CONIINE
CURARE
CYANIDE
DATURA
DIOXIN
EMETINE
ERGOT
HEBONA
LEAD
MEZEREON

OUABAIN
OURALI
PHALLIN
PHENOL
SARIN
SASSWOOD
SOMAN
THALLIUM
TIMBO
TOXAPHENE

D	T	R	K	S	E	A	S	T	A	L	L	I	O	N
Y	N	A	R	C	T	U	R	U	S	G	N	S	R	Y
E	H	N	O	D	I	E	S	O	P	T	A	E	B	D
R	E	E	C	H	I	N	O	O	K	N	I	A	C	A
P	R	O	D	A	R	B	A	L	C	R	C	R	K	L
S	C	A	U	R	O	R	A	L	R	A	R	A	I	N
O	U	V	I	P	E	R	I	A	Y	R	U	N	O	O
S	L	G	N	F	O	P	H	U	E	X	H	G	W	G
I	E	A	C	T	P	A	S	D	T	C	G	E	A	A
O	S	L	P	E	W	E	N	E	N	M	O	R	C	R
U	H	A	R	K	T	E	N	E	I	O	O	B	G	D
Q	R	X	E	E	T	R	L	R	R	R	L	N	R	G
O	S	Y	X	X	O	G	H	A	I	F	A	A	E	A
R	E	A	E	H	A	P	R	O	W	L	E	R	T	V
I	N	R	A	E	A	R	N	D	R	A	V	R	A	H

MODERN US MILITARY AIRCRAFT

ARCTURUS	GALAXY	OSPREY
ARIES	HARRIER	POSEIDON
AURORA	HARVARD	PROWLER
CAYUSE	HAWKEYE	RAPTOR
CHINOOK	HERCULES	SEA RANGER
CLIPPER	HORNET	SEA STALLION
COBRA	IROQUOIS	TALON
DRAGON LADY	KIOWA	TEXAN
EAGLE	LABRADOR	VENOM
EXTENDER	ORION	VIPER

D	F	I	E	L	D	H	O	C	K	E	Y	E	M	G
W	E	I	G	H	T	L	I	F	T	I	N	G	O	N
T	R	I	A	T	H	L	O	N	G	F	G	A	U	I
T	M	R	L	T	F	L	C	X	N	E	N	S	N	P
A	I	S	W	N	H	I	O	I	I	N	I	S	T	M
E	S	G	A	S	O	L	E	I	W	C	L	E	A	U
K	H	N	I	I	C	T	E	G	O	I	C	R	I	J
W	O	I	V	H	L	I	N	T	R	N	Y	D	N	B
O	O	X	L	S	A	I	T	I	I	G	C	I	B	M
N	T	O	L	L	M	N	N	S	M	C	O	I	I	X
D	I	B	T	M	T	A	D	G	A	D	S	T	K	I
O	N	D	I	V	I	N	G	B	U	N	A	M	I	E
O	G	W	C	T	N	O	N	J	A	D	M	B	N	O
R	S	B	A	S	K	E	T	B	A	L	L	Y	G	O
K	G	G	N	I	T	N	E	V	E	G	L	E	G	T

WATCHING THE OLYMPICS

ATHLETICS
BADMINTON
BASKETBALL
BMX
BOXING
CYCLING
DIVING
DRESSAGE

EVENTING
FENCING
FIELD HOCKEY
GYMNASTICS
HANDBALL
JUDO
JUMPING
MOUNTAIN BIKING

ROWING
SAILING
SHOOTING
SWIMMING
TAE KWON DO
TRIATHLON
WEIGHTLIFTING

E	N	O	I	T	A	L	L	E	C	N	A	C	E	G
T	K	S	N	C	A	T	P	L	A	T	F	O	R	M
R	N	R	F	I	R	S	T	C	L	A	S	S	L	R
N	O	I	T	A	T	S	C	T	V	S	A	Y	R	E
D	I	S	I	E	A	F	A	D	T	R	A	C	K	S
R	A	R	F	I	T	T	R	S	A	L	T	A	E	S
A	W	S	I	I	E	I	S	D	E	N	A	E	D	C
U	R	M	W	K	V	E	A	D	R	S	V	S	L	E
G	A	S	C	E	R	Y	E	R	I	E	I	D	S	S
N	I	I	R	P	T	T	N	R	S	T	R	T	R	R
A	T	V	X	R	I	E	G	G	A	N	S	U	O	T
O	D	E	I	T	O	L	O	C	A	L	R	L	R	A
L	E	P	S	R	E	G	N	E	S	S	A	P	E	N
F	R	L	C	N	O	I	T	A	V	R	E	S	E	R
X	Y	N	D	E	S	T	I	N	A	T	I	O	N	M

RAILWAY JOURNEY

CANCELLATION
DAY TRIP
DELAY
DESTINATION
DRIVER
EXPRESS
FIRST CLASS

GUARD
LOCAL
PASSENGERS
PLATFORM
RESERVATION
RETURN
SEAT

SINGLE
STATION
TICKET
TRACKS
WI-FI

```
O R O C I L E G N A I L L O I
T M H E A L B E R T I O K A T
T N A O T C L R T R E H C S E
E P G S C N E E E O T R E H S
R I I I S K M S C O M A K R G
O S P I O O N Y R I M W E E D
T A G P C T N E R E T I B E E
N N C A I L T K Y A N T N O K
I O I H O L C O T E E I O L O
T G B B A C O N T A L B E B O
O E R I I G E E L K O O U C N
U L E A H P A R I S R O L R I
N B L A K E H L C T I T I A N
I N S H A W G H L E R O O M G
N R I L E Y G H I B E R T I I
```

ARTISTS

ALBERTI
ANGELICO
BACON
BLAKE
BOSCH
BOTTICELLI
CHAGALL
DE KOONING
ESCHER
GHIBERTI

GIACOMETTI
GIOTTO
HOCKNEY
INSHAW
KEYSER
KLEE
KLINE
LIPPI
MAES
MASSON

MOORE
PISANO
RAEBURN
RAPHAEL
RILEY
ROTHKO
TENIERS
TINTORETTO
TITIAN
WARHOL

Y	E	O	S	P	I	N	Y	H	E	A	D	E	D	B
O	C	K	M	H	T	M	N	W	F	E	E	E	R	D
E	R	C	U	W	R	I	N	E	E	T	B	A	U	I
A	R	M	A	L	O	K	R	R	E	N	R	U	G	D
T	U	E	R	N	F	R	R	D	O	E	X	K	T	D
C	N	M	U	O	C	T	R	D	I	C	E	E	L	B
E	L	N	T	R	W	I	O	A	L	E	A	N	A	F
W	B	A	N	H	O	K	E	N	R	E	R	L	E	I
A	I	O	M	M	L	D	O	I	G	E	R	E	L	A
E	E	R	K	A	O	T	B	O	O	U	W	L	N	E
B	N	P	B	T	R	B	E	E	H	A	E	Y	E	N
T	U	A	A	E	O	B	T	U	B	I	F	E	X	I
O	F	M	D	N	H	C	E	E	L	F	A	E	N	U
E	E	T	L	B	L	A	D	D	E	R	K	A	M	G
N	D	E	W	E	T	N	A	E	T	R	E	M	E	N

TYPES OF WORM

ACORN	FLUKE	NEREID
ARROW	GUINEA	RIBBON
BLADDER	HOOKWORM	SPINY-HEADED
CLAM	LEECH	TONGUE
DEW	NEMATODE	TUBE
FAN	NEMERTEAN	TUBIFEX

D	E	A	A	T	R	A	I	L	S	I	D	E	O	C
E	F	A	L	C	A	T	E	T	B	B	E	L	U	S
T	S	Y	K	A	E	R	T	S	L	R	L	A	G	H
T	P	L	M	I	M	O	S	A	U	I	W	O	D	O
O	I	M	A	N	U	E	L	S	R	H	L	A	E	R
P	K	W	A	N	E	F	S	T	I	D	D	Y	D	T
S	E	I	C	E	L	E	O	T	E	E	S	A	N	T
R	B	N	A	S	T	P	E	N	L	T	A	T	A	A
E	A	D	C	Z	W	T	B	Z	A	N	A	S	B	I
V	N	D	I	O	A	A	Z	R	O	R	Y	O	S	L
L	D	R	A	C	N	I	R	Z	C	R	A	C	O	E
I	E	R	I	D	R	E	I	T	A	D	V	D	S	D
S	D	L	E	G	D	R	I	O	H	C	A	L	I	R
W	E	D	O	S	A	C	H	O	E	Y	U	O	H	I
D	S	M	E	R	C	U	R	I	A	L	G	G	C	R

SKIPPER BUTTERFLIES

ACACIA
ARCTIC
ARIZONA
BELUS
CHISOS BANDED
DELICATE
FALCATE
GOLD-COSTA
GOLDEN BANDED

GRIZZLED
GUAVA
HOARY
MANUEL'S
MERCURIAL
MIMOSA
POTRILLO
RUSSET
SHORT-TAILED

SILVER-SPOTTED
SPIKE BANDED
STARRED
STREAKY
SWARTHY
TRAILSIDE
WHITE
WIND

M	Y	Y	T	E	R	G	E	R	L	U	S	T	M	T
R	H	S	T	S	E	R	E	T	N	I	A	I	I	H
A	T	E	N	V	Y	T	I	L	I	T	S	O	H	A
L	A	A	N	N	O	Y	A	N	C	E	P	E	P	N
A	P	P	Y	A	H	T	R	H	R	T	E	S	I	K
F	M	G	P	T	B	D	H	Y	Y	W	D	I	T	F
F	Y	O	L	R	E	H	A	G	A	T	I	R	Y	U
E	S	H	O	S	E	I	O	E	I	T	R	P	G	L
C	T	G	V	R	R	H	X	R	R	R	P	R	U	N
T	R	E	E	O	E	E	N	R	D	F	U	I	E
I	T	R	R	C	U	D	M	N	A	E	H	S	L	S
O	I	R	I	R	I	S	N	O	S	G	N	A	T	S
N	O	N	H	D	O	E	S	O	R	I	T	C	S	H
H	A	D	E	S	I	R	E	G	W	S	O	S	E	V
P	A	S	S	R	I	A	P	S	E	D	E	N	S	P

EMOTIONS

ABHORRENCE
AFFECTION
ALARM
ANNOYANCE
ANXIETY
APPREHENSION
AWE
DESIRE
DESPAIR
DREAD

ENVY
FRIGHT
GUILT
HATE
HORROR
HOSTILITY
INTEREST
LOVE
LUST
MISERY

PANIC
PITY
PRIDE
REGRET
REMORSE
SURPRISE
SYMPATHY
TERROR
THANKFULNESS
WONDER

T	A	E	R	G	E	H	T	R	E	T	E	P	H	O
R	A	A	Z	G	E	N	G	H	I	S	K	H	A	N
A	L	E	M	E	S	A	N	S	U	U	K	Y	I	T
S	C	L	R	V	L	M	R	A	D	A	M	S	N	H
E	H	H	E	G	O	I	A	T	G	R	B	R	L	A
A	U	M	A	W	E	N	Z	N	A	N	T	C	O	T
C	R	E	U	R	M	H	B	A	D	P	I	M	C	C
S	C	R	T	I	L	O	T	I	B	E	O	K	N	H
U	H	K	I	O	T	E	R	D	S	E	L	E	I	E
I	I	E	P	I	T	T	M	C	E	M	T	A	L	R
L	L	L	H	O	R	T	S	A	C	R	A	H	N	C
U	L	G	A	N	D	H	I	K	G	O	F	R	I	E
J	N	O	S	R	E	F	F	E	J	N	A	L	C	N
V	I	C	T	O	R	I	A	H	E	M	E	M	A	K
A	T	L	E	V	E	S	O	O	R	E	A	G	A	N

FAMOUS LEADERS

ADAMS
ALFRED THE GREAT
CASTRO
CHARLEMAGNE
CHURCHILL
CLEOPATRA
CROMWELL
ELIZABETH I
GANDHI

GENGHIS KHAN
JEFFERSON
JULIUS CAESAR
KING
LINCOLN
MANDELA
MAO
MERKEL
PETER THE GREAT

PITT
REAGAN
ROOSEVELT
SAN SUU KYI
THATCHER
VICTORIA
VON BISMARCK

YOGA POSES

BOW	DANCER	PEACOCK
CAMEL	FISH	PENDANT
CAT	HALF MOON	RABBIT
CHILD	HERON	RECLINING HERO
COBRA	INSECT	SCORPION
COCKEREL	LION	THUNDERBOLT
COW FACE	LOCUST	TORTOISE
CRANE	LOTUS	TREE
CROCODILE	MONKEY	TRIANGLE
CROSS	MOUNTAIN	WARRIOR

SAUCES

BARBECUE	CURRY	PASSATA
BEARNAISE	FISH	PESTO
BLACK BEAN	FONDUE	PIRI-PIRI
BOLOGNESE	HOISIN	SALSA
BREAD	KETCHUP	SATAY
CAPER	MARINARA	SOY
CARBONARA	MOLE	TOMATO
CHASSEUR	MORNAY	
CHEESE	OYSTER	

S	B	S	Y	A	R	U	L	B	E	K	A	S	E	S
N	E	P	L	A	Y	I	N	G	C	A	R	D	S	D
H	C	H	O	C	O	L	A	T	E	S	T	D	S	K
S	F	U	T	T	Z	L	N	B	T	T	S	B	E	K
E	E	L	N	O	E	C	D	G	E	S	U	O	I	O
B	N	I	O	D	L	L	O	P	W	L	B	I	R	O
O	A	I	L	W	E	C	B	O	A	S	S	E	O	B
O	O	D	Z	P	E	R	T	A	S	O	C	G	S	E
K	E	V	S	A	P	R	W	O	T	C	R	I	S	L
S	S	D	A	E	G	U	S	E	Y	K	I	F	E	Z
P	L	A	N	T	O	A	S	P	A	S	P	T	C	Z
A	G	S	R	A	G	H	M	T	O	R	T	C	C	U
E	M	U	F	R	E	P	S	R	R	I	A	A	P
C	E	R	A	W	K	O	O	C	C	A	O	R	G	N
B	B	O	A	R	D	G	A	M	E	L	N	D	S	R

CHRISTMAS PRESENTS

ACCESSORIES
ART SUPPLIES
BLU-RAYS
BOARD GAME
BOOKS
CHOCOLATES
CLOTHES
COOKWARE

DVD
FLOWERS
GIFT CARD
MAGAZINE
PERFUME
PET
PLANT
PLAYING CARDS

PUZZLE BOOK
SHOES
SOCKS
SUBSCRIPTION
TABLET
TOYS
UNDERWEAR

S	G	P	Y	C	N	Y	S	L	Y	N	P	Y	L	S
L	H	S	H	R	L	Y	L	M	P	S	Y	Z	X	T
L	Y	Y	T	H	N	C	G	F	S	L	L	C	Y	Y
S	L	C	Y	M	R	Y	S	T	H	Y	M	N	Y	L
T	L	H	M	Y	P	S	L	Y	S	Y	L	P	H	R
P	M	Y	P	H	S	R	P	M	S	Y	B	T	S	H
S	Y	T	L	P	L	L	Y	Y	Y	Y	R	Y	Y	Y
M	H	X	W	Y	N	D	N	L	H	S	R	L	T	T
Y	G	N	N	Y	F	T	Y	Y	Y	Y	R	Y	R	H
R	P	B	H	Y	H	M	G	W	L	R	M	R	Y	M
R	G	Y	M	Z	L	Y	R	Y	H	Y	P	D	S	H
H	H	W	Y	F	P	Y	Y	Y	F	M	H	S	T	M
C	R	T	R	S	L	L	Y	G	Y	Z	Y	S	P	M
Y	M	Y	Y	Y	T	W	H	Y	Y	M	Y	P	C	Y
Y	L	M	T	S	L	T	L	H	C	N	Y	L	M	B

VOWELLESS WORDS

BRRR	LYNCH	SPRYLY
CRYPT	LYNX	STY
DRYLY	MYRRH	SYLPH
FLY	MYTH	SYNC
FRY	PSST	SYNTH
GHYLL	PSYCH	SYZYGY
GYM	PYGMY	TRYST
GYPSY	RHYTHM	WHY
HMM	SHYLY	WRYLY
HYMN	SLYLY	WYND

S	P	A	K	K	W	L	C	H	U	T	N	E	Y	O
S	W	I	L	P	O	T	A	T	O	S	A	L	A	D
A	E	M	C	S	S	T	O	R	R	A	C	N	E
N	U	E	N	K	L	O	R	T	E	U	C	A	A	E
D	H	A	M	E	L	C	C	O	L	E	S	L	A	W
W	I	Y	C	G	K	E	A	S	S	L	E	H	A	I
I	C	C	S	E	E	C	H	K	K	H	E	M	S	A
C	L	U	E	L	S	E	I	E	E	S	P	E	L	Y
H	H	C	I	N	F	E	B	H	C	R	V	U	A	C
E	U	U	R	S	S	A	E	E	C	I	M	D	H	G
S	M	M	T	T	B	A	L	H	L	F	R	U	I	T
C	M	B	S	S	A	E	O	O	C	W	L	L	H	C
D	U	E	A	U	R	A	S	R	O	L	L	S	A	O
E	S	R	P	Y	L	L	E	M	O	N	A	D	E	L
C	U	O	G	R	E	E	N	S	A	L	A	D	U	A

PICNIC FOOD

CAKE	COLESLAW	LEMONADE
CARROTS	CUCUMBER	OLIVES
CELERY	FRUIT	PASTRIES
CHEESE	GREEN SALAD	PICKLE
CHICKEN	HAM	POTATO SALAD
CHUTNEY	HUMMUS	ROLLS
COLA	KEBABS	SANDWICHES

JAZZ MUSICIANS

BASIE
BECHET
BIX
BLAKEY
BRUBECK
COLEMAN
COLTRANE
DANKWORTH
DAVIS
FITZGERALD

GARNER
GETZ
GORDON
GRAPPELLI
HADEN
HAMPTON
HAWKINS
JARRETT
LYTTELTON
MARSALIS

MINGUS
OLIVER
PETERSON
PINE
SHAW
TATUM
VAUGHAN
WALLER

U	Y	T	R	C	S	E	R	E	D	D	E	R	H	S
K	V	D	H	E	N	C	C	M	X	S	W	T	A	B
F	I	R	O	A	G	M	A	A	O	U	D	R	A	E
E	N	E	D	C	N	A	Y	R	R	N	A	N	E	S
T	O	D	R	O	T	O	L	S	E	N	E	M	M	P
H	S	S	O	E	Z	O	S	A	T	C	A	V	O	Y
E	I	K	H	O	E	L	R	O	C	I	R	G	R	L
R	O	U	T	E	M	R	A	O	T	T	Q	O	E	A
I	P	L	U	H	Z	S	E	R	C	E	U	U	W	C
D	I	L	L	T	E	E	D	C	E	T	N	S	E	O
D	K	U	X	L	L	J	E	A	A	N	O	G	O	P
L	O	Y	E	C	R	K	O	R	Y	F	E	P	A	A
E	L	F	L	T	K	I	A	K	F	E	O	G	U	M
R	N	I	L	B	O	G	N	E	E	R	G	W	T	S
N	I	U	G	N	E	P	E	H	T	R	M	G	T	V

SUPERHERO VILLAINS

APOCALYPSE
BANE
CARNAGE
DOCTOR OCTOPUS
DOOMSDAY
GALACTUS
GENERAL ZOD
GREEN GOBLIN

LEX LUTHOR
LOKI
MAGNETO
MR FREEZE
MYSTIQUE
POISON IVY
RED SKULL
SCARECROW

SHREDDER
THANOS
THE JOKER
THE PENGUIN
THE RIDDLER
TWO-FACE
VENOM

GADGETS

CALCULATOR
CAMCORDER
CAMERA
DRONE
EARPIECE
E-BOOK READER
FITNESS TRACKER

GAMES CONSOLE
GPS TRACKER
LAPTOP
PEDOMETER
PRINTER
SATNAV
SCANNER

SEGWAY
SPEAKERS
TABLET
TELEVISION
VR GOGGLES
WATCH

WORDS WITH 'WORD' IN

BACKSWORD
BROADSWORD
BUZZWORD
BYWORD
CATCHWORD
FOREWORD
HEADWORD
KEYWORD
LOANWORD

MISWORD
PASSWORD
SMALLSWORD
SWEARWORD
SWORDFISH
SWORDLESS
SWORDPLAY
WATCHWORD
WORDAGE

WORDED
WORDIER
WORDILY
WORDING
WORDLESSLY
WORDLORE
WORDMONGER
WORDSMITH
WORDY

U	P	M	O	R	P	H	E	U	S	E	Z	S	N	S
Z	S	U	R	A	D	O	N	I	S	N	S	U	D	U
S	E	H	Y	O	A	E	S	S	A	S	O	N	I	I
E	H	U	U	L	T	S	O	P	O	A	T	A	O	P
R	E	E	S	L	S	E	A	N	U	H	A	R	N	E
A	P	C	O	O	A	O	P	A	E	A	N	U	Y	L
L	H	R	U	P	E	Y	R	R	G	R	A	A	S	C
S	A	O	S	A	H	T	M	E	I	R	H	T	U	S
I	E	N	D	O	C	E	A	N	U	S	T	L	S	A
T	S	U	S	Y	S	T	O	H	E	L	H	A	U	A
T	T	S	O	O	H	T	A	E	R	R	O	S	N	E
A	U	S	I	S	A	D	U	N	S	O	E	S	A	O
A	S	S	L	U	E	S	A	E	R	O	B	U	J	L
N	P	S	E	S	P	O	S	E	I	D	O	N	S	U
N	S	I	H	R	L	G	A	N	Y	M	E	D	E	S

GREEK GODS

ADONIS
AEOLUS
APOLLO
ARES
ASCLEPIUS
ATLAS
ATTIS
BOREAS
CRONUS

DIONYSUS
EROS
GANYMEDE
HADES
HELIOS
HEPHAESTUS
HERMES
HYPNOS
JANUS

MORPHEUS
NEREUS
OCEANUS
PAN
POSEIDON
THANATOS
URANUS
ZEUS

R	E	I	D	E	N	T	I	F	Y	E	B	F	U	Z
K	W	A	H	A	N	D	L	E	N	E	E	V	A	S
R	R	E	C	O	R	D	R	O	M	A	R	C	H	L
A	L	L	O	W	R	S	H	T	S	C	R	E	A	M
P	L	K	L	P	E	P	H	R	A	E	S	N	L	H
S	L	S	L	E	E	A	E	A	E	E	I	B	E	L
S	I	V	C	L	D	A	K	D	R	A	T	S	L	R
S	A	L	E	R	N	H	L	M	R	E	M	P	D	E
A	W	T	R	S	A	L	A	I	N	L	P	A	D	T
I	H	V	S	E	L	T	W	R	N	E	A	I	A	S
L	S	A	H	R	T	E	C	E	K	P	T	N	P	A
S	P	S	B	U	R	C	S	H	A	A	E	T	N	P
M	A	T	C	H	M	A	R	R	Y	C	A	D	T	L
W	S	H	G	U	A	L	O	R	E	S	S	M	A	E
J	A	M	S	A	A	E	T	A	M	E	E	A	M	I

REGULAR VERBS

ADMIRE	MATCH	SAVE
ALLOW	MATE	SCRATCH
ESCAPE	PADDLE	SCREAM
HANDLE	PAINT	SCRUB
IDENTIFY	PARK	SHARE
JAM	PASS	TEASE
LAND	PASTE	TELEPHONE
LAUGH	RAIN	WAIL
MARCH	RECORD	WALK
MARRY	SAIL	WASH

N	R	E	C	O	C	T	E	A	U	D	B	H	L	J
E	R	A	E	P	S	E	K	A	H	S	K	T	Y	O
N	E	S	B	I	L	T	W	N	M	A	T	E	I	N
G	C	M	M	O	D	I	T	I	O	E	N	N	A	S
O	O	A	A	B	L	N	L	C	K	A	T	R	E	O
E	W	R	M	D	N	L	E	C	L	N	H	U	N	N
T	A	L	E	B	E	L	E	E	M	E	C	O	R	R
H	R	O	T	R	I	B	D	A	L	D	E	B	O	E
E	D	W	V	O	H	K	E	H	C	R	R	K	B	L
D	S	E	T	G	S	S	H	A	W	A	B	C	S	L
R	M	I	D	D	L	E	T	O	N	P	O	Y	O	I
L	P	R	I	E	S	T	L	E	Y	P	R	A	T	H
F	O	A	O	T	W	A	Y	C	C	O	T	R	A	C
T	N	P	E	E	R	T	R	A	S	T	O	S	D	S
W	A	K	B	E	R	K	O	F	F	S	N	R	T	Y

PLAYWRIGHTS

ARDEN	ELIOT	OSBORNE
AYCKBOURN	GOETHE	OTWAY
BECKETT	IBSEN	PRIESTLEY
BERKOFF	JONSON	SARTRE
BRECHT	MAMET	SCHILLER
CHEKHOV	MARLOWE	SHAKESPEARE
COCTEAU	MIDDLETON	SHAW
COWARD	MILLER	STOPPARD
DELANEY	ORTON	WILDE

C	L	A	N	C	H	A	L	C	I	D	I	A	N	I
U	O	I	A	H	B	E	L	E	I	K	O	F	H	A
N	G	H	I	R	N	R	E	G	E	A	U	K	N	R
E	O	K	G	I	U	R	A	E	I	T	S	A	S	A
I	G	U	R	K	R	N	R	E	H	A	G	P	H	B
F	R	M	O	S	I	G	I	A	N	A	I	I	P	I
O	A	R	E	Y	F	D	R	C	R	I	L	C	Y	C
R	P	U	G	L	I	K	E	I	A	H	L	T	L	Y
M	H	G	C	L	N	A	H	O	E	I	L	O	G	R
N	R	N	I	A	G	R	I	B	G	H	O	G	O	I
A	O	I	S	B	E	A	R	A	R	R	G	R	R	L
M	M	J	S	A	R	E	B	H	S	A	A	A	E	L
O	A	N	O	R	W	N	G	I	R	A	L	P	I	I
R	J	A	L	Y	C	I	F	U	K	F	G	H	H	C
I	I	K	G	I	O	L	E	G	N	A	R	T	S	E

ALPHABETS

ARABIC
CHALCIDIAN
CUNEIFORM
CYRILLIC
ESTRANGELO
FINGER
FUTHARK
GEORGIAN
GLAGOL

GLOSSIC
GREEK
GURMUKHI
HEBREW
HIEROGLYPHS
HIRAGANA
IDEOGRAPH
KANJI
KUFIC

LINEAR A
LINEAR B
LOGOGRAPH
NASKHI
PICTOGRAPH
ROMAJI
ROMAN
RUNIC
SYLLABARY

S	E	L	E	T	N	I	L	M	R	E	B	M	I	T
O	L	M	T	T	O	T	L	A	H	P	S	A	U	L
T	G	E	N	U	R	Y	U	S	A	B	B	O	R	L
S	N	E	E	S	I	A	R	T	W	T	R	C	O	E
E	I	R	M	T	T	L	E	I	L	G	I	D	O	N
B	H	A	E	R	S	C	R	C	C	T	C	O	F	O
S	S	T	C	A	A	S	C	O	S	A	K	O	T	T
A	H	R	E	L	C	V	S	A	I	A	O	W	I	S
N	C	O	H	H	A	T	L	E	M	V	R	Y	L	G
D	T	M	D	S	B	P	R	A	L	R	A	L	E	N
S	A	E	T	A	L	S	B	B	G	N	A	P	T	I
T	H	E	L	B	R	A	M	O	L	G	I	T	I	V
O	T	G	R	A	N	I	T	E	A	N	I	A	M	A
N	M	U	S	P	Y	G	G	O	S	R	A	N	T	P
E	T	E	R	C	N	O	C	E	S	O	D	L	G	S

BUILDING MATERIALS

ASBESTOS
ASHLAR
ASPHALT
BRICK
CAST IRON
CEMENT
CLAPBOARD
CLAY
CONCRETE
GLASS

GRANITE
GROUT
GYPSUM
LAGGING
LINTEL
MARBLE
MASTIC
MORTAR
PAVING STONE
PAVIOR

PLASTIC
PLYWOOD
ROOF TILE
SANDSTONE
SHINGLE
SLATE
STAINLESS STEEL
TARMAC
THATCH
TIMBER

O	O	S	C	C	K	C	O	L	R	A	H	C	P	O
L	I	O	F	E	U	Q	N	I	C	U	S	S	O	M
E	S	C	A	C	L	E	A	V	E	R	S	D	W	N
O	O	E	T	W	B	U	T	T	E	R	C	U	P	S
T	D	T	H	I	P	E	A	R	L	W	O	R	T	P
C	D	E	E	R	N	O	M	M	O	C	E	O	A	E
P	L	E	N	N	L	D	E	E	W	G	A	R	L	E
B	O	O	R	O	R	W	O	R	R	A	Y	I	S	D
B	O	N	V	A	A	U	E	X	R	O	A	P	E	W
U	R	D	D	E	T	D	B	I	A	T	B	E	L	E
R	E	A	N	W	R	Y	B	D	E	L	W	R	F	L
D	B	I	C	S	E	W	R	S	A	X	I	I	H	L
O	B	S	W	K	O	E	R	I	I	L	I	S	E	N
C	I	Y	C	R	E	O	D	L	A	O	A	R	A	O
K	V	E	T	C	H	N	F	B	E	H	L	S	L	N

WEEDS

BRACKEN	DAISY	PONDWEED
BURDOCK	FAT HEN	RAGWEED
BUTTERCUP	FLIXWEED	RIBWORT
CHARLOCK	HAIRY TARE	SALAD BURNET
CINQUEFOIL	HORSETAIL	SELFHEAL
CLEAVERS	MOSS	SPEEDWELL
CLOVER	OXALIS	VETCH
COMMON REED	PEARLWORT	YARROW

MAKE A GETAWAY

ABSCOND
BOLT
CUT AND RUN
DECAMP
DEPART
DISAPPEAR
ESCAPE
FLEE

GET OUT
HIT THE ROAD
LEAVE
MAKE A BREAK FOR IT
MAKE TRACKS
RETREAT
RUSH
SCOOT

SCRAM
SHOVE OFF
SKEDADDLE
SPLIT
TAKE OFF
VAMOOSE
VANISH

G	G	E	N	O	T	S	K	C	O	H	C	T	I	P
E	N	I	Y	R	O	P	H	S	S	E	T	E	R	A
P	I	R	E	N	E	U	C	U	G	N	S	S	A	I
O	L	O	N	U	T	R	M	D	O	T	N	N	F	A
R	S	P	M	M	E	M	I	P	A	O	O	F	R	P
C	T	E	I	E	I	R	M	N	W	T	I	E	I	L
I	S	S	H	T	B	A	D	C	I	L	D	C	O	N
M	I	L	C	W	R	I	O	P	C	N	K	C	T	T
A	R	I	O	C	N	R	D	K	E	T	Y	E	Y	U
N	W	N	H	G	N	E	L	C	S	N	L	R	I	O
Y	S	G	R	I	G	A	S	R	T	U	L	U	N	P
D	A	O	C	N	H	E	E	A	E	H	U	S	G	O
N	P	E	I	C	D	T	O	G	P	S	G	S	I	T
E	P	R	S	E	L	F	B	E	L	A	Y	I	N	G
S	E	L	G	G	O	G	W	O	N	S	H	F	S	E

GONE CLIMBING

ARETE
CHALK CLIFF
CHIMNEY
CHOCKSTONE
COL
CRAG
CRAMPON
DESCENDER
DYNAMIC ROPE
FISSURE

GULLY
HUT
ICE STEP
MUNRO
PICK
PITCH
RINGED PITON
ROPE SLING
SCREE
SELF-BELAYING

SHUNT
SNOW BRIDGE
SNOW CORNICE
SNOW GOGGLES
SPUR
STANDING ROPE
SUMMIT
TOP OUT
TYING IN
WRIST SLING

E	C	T	A	T	S	O	M	R	E	H	T	G	R	D
P	O	J	P	S	P	D	O	R	N	I	A	R	D	B
I	U	R	K	K	N	A	T	R	E	D	A	E	H	A
P	P	E	E	T	A	B	R	E	J	E	D	R	N	C
R	L	T	L	C	E	R	A	T	D	O	N	E	R	K
E	E	A	B	F	S	V	E	L	P	A	E	S	E	B
P	R	E	O	L	R	N	L	P	L	K	B	Y	T	O
P	R	H	W	O	V	A	I	A	P	V	U	E	S	I
O	E	R	J	A	H	O	D	A	V	O	A	G	I	L
C	D	E	O	T	O	T	T	I	M	E	H	L	C	E
P	N	T	I	T	S	N	A	E	A	R	T	U	V	R
L	I	A	N	W	E	D	P	C	K	T	E	A	L	E
U	L	W	T	N	E	V	L	I	O	S	O	T	G	A
G	Y	D	R	A	I	N	C	O	C	K	A	R	A	A
O	C	T	E	P	I	P	E	T	S	A	W	G	C	W

CALL A PLUMBER

BACK BOILER
BALL VALVE
CISTERN
COPPER PIPE
COUPLER
CYLINDER
DRAINCOCK
DRAIN ROD
ELBOW JOINT
FLOAT
GASKET
GATE VALVE
GEYSER
HEADER TANK
HOPPER
HOSE
PLUG
P-TRAP
RADIATOR
SOIL VENT
THERMOSTAT
U-BEND
WASTE PIPE
WATER HEATER
WATER MAINS

ASIAN COUNTRIES

BAHRAIN	JAPAN	NORTH KOREA
BANGLADESH	JORDAN	OMAN
BHUTAN	KYRGYZSTAN	QATAR
BRUNEI	LAOS	SOUTH KOREA
CAMBODIA	LEBANON	SRI LANKA
CHINA	MALAYSIA	SYRIA
INDIA	MALDIVES	TAJIKISTAN
IRAN	MONGOLIA	TIMOR-LESTE
IRAQ	MYANMAR	YEMEN
ISRAEL	NEPAL	

L	Y	L	F	N	O	G	A	R	D	E	R	S	B	L
A	R	B	R	H	O	R	S	E	F	L	Y	A	E	Y
A	B	I	L	H	M	T	E	N	R	O	H	N	E	L
R	E	P	P	O	H	S	S	A	R	G	A	L	W	F
Y	G	C	T	V	D	L	A	R	E	M	E	A	B	R
L	N	E	E	E	R	H	E	O	T	G	S	U	D	E
F	I	T	H	R	K	F	N	A	P	P	T	T	A	E
N	W	E	E	F	P	C	O	F	R	T	C	A	M	D
E	E	R	E	L	C	B	I	E	E	W	A	N	S	T
E	C	E	O	Y	R	A	C	R	E	L	I	G	E	R
R	A	T	N	E	P	R	F	W	C	A	T	G	L	E
G	L	R	T	H	Y	L	F	E	P	I	N	S	F	K
R	P	A	I	E	Y	L	F	Y	A	M	A	S	L	W
S	W	D	N	L	A	Y	L	F	W	A	S	N	Y	A
L	R	B	L	H	C	A	O	R	K	C	O	C	E	H

BRITISH INSECTS

ANT
APHID
BEE
BUTTERFLY
COCKROACH
CRICKET
DAMSELFLY
DARTER
DEER FLY

DRAGONFLY
EARWIG
EMERALD
GNAT
GRASSHOPPER
GREENFLY
HAWKER
HORNET
HORSEFLY

HOVERFLY
LACEWING
MAYFLY
SAWFLY
SNIPE FLY
WASP
WATER BOATMAN

Y	D	E	N	N	E	K	U	R	N	A	M	U	R	T
C	B	Y	O	R	R	E	W	O	H	N	E	S	I	E
A	D	W	E	D	C	C	O	O	L	I	D	G	E	E
P	M	R	A	L	L	A	A	T	R	U	M	P	O	O
O	S	A	O	S	N	E	R	C	S	S	M	A	D	A
R	T	M	B	F	H	I	I	T	W	I	L	S	O	N
E	S	A	T	O	N	I	K	F	E	E	N	H	O	R
A	C	L	I	N	T	O	N	C	R	R	E	S	F	E
G	L	I	N	C	O	L	N	G	M	A	N	U	N	V
A	M	O	N	R	O	E	T	B	T	H	G	B	Y	O
N	B	U	C	H	A	N	A	N	O	O	E	V	O	O
M	A	D	I	S	O	N	R	J	N	L	N	D	U	H
O	N	I	X	O	N	T	L	E	V	E	S	O	O	R
N	O	S	R	E	F	F	E	J	R	N	A	O	R	E
H	E	J	A	C	K	S	O	N	O	T	N	A	R	G

US PRESIDENTS

ADAMS
BUCHANAN
BUSH
CARTER
CLINTON
COOLIDGE
EISENHOWER
FORD
GARFIELD

GRANT
HOOVER
JACKSON
JEFFERSON
JOHNSON
KENNEDY
LINCOLN
MADISON
MCKINLEY

MONROE
NIXON
OBAMA
REAGAN
ROOSEVELT
TRUMAN
TRUMP
WASHINGTON
WILSON

```
S E M M R F I R E A L A R M G
L L R R H R E P E E L B D G N
G A A A E L A K S Z Y D O N R
N N L L R F U I K K Z N A R O
I G A A A T U O H S G U O O H
N I E Y L O N A O F L G B H R
R S K T F K M T S I R E N G A
A S O I O I L A G O R O R O C
W S M R S B O A Y A A O R F F
M E S U E S E N X D L L E A E
R R T C N G O L L O A F C M S
O T G E R C B N L O N Y D O S
T S F S A E A L R R Y E S E I
S I N E R E D L I G H T O N R
W D B L A N G I S E K O M S R
```

ALARM SIGNALS

BEACON
BELL
BLEEPER
BUZZER
CAR HORN
DISTRESS SIGNAL
FIRE ALARM

FLARE
FOGHORN
GONG
KLAXON
MAYDAY
RED FLAG
RED LIGHT

SECURITY ALARM
SHOUT
SIREN
SMOKE ALARM
SMOKE SIGNAL
SOS
STORM WARNING

D	E	R	R	C	R	E	N	N	U	R	D	A	O	R
P	S	X	Y	R	O	L	R	E	P	I	V	Y	S	N
S	I	D	H	H	H	A	J	L	E	R	K	H	Y	B
A	O	A	L	I	H	T	A	R	A	N	T	U	L	A
N	T	N	T	N	C	V	C	O	B	R	A	E	E	I
D	R	T	H	O	I	U	K	O	E	L	T	A	I	N
C	O	E	A	C	R	L	A	H	A	N	F	S	L	O
A	T	L	T	E	T	T	L	C	A	L	T	P	A	I
T	A	O	E	R	S	U	A	H	O	E	R	R	A	L
J	K	P	E	O	O	R	P	W	R	M	X	I	N	O
A	R	E	H	S	A	E	D	E	A	A	T	N	E	K
T	E	O	C	C	L	R	H	O	D	C	R	G	Y	E
C	E	N	C	E	A	F	U	D	A	R	M	B	H	W
R	M	E	R	A	D	R	A	P	O	E	L	O	E	A
A	G	R	A	S	S	H	O	P	P	E	R	K	L	Z

DESERT ANIMALS

AARDWOLF
ADDAX
ANTELOPE
CAMEL
CARACAL
CHEETAH
COBRA
ELEPHANT
GRASSHOPPER

HYENA
JACKAL
LEOPARD
LION
MEERKAT
ORYX
OSTRICH
RHINOCEROS
ROADRUNNER

SAND CAT
SPRINGBOK
TARANTULA
TORTOISE
VIPER
VULTURE
ZEBRA

```
G  M  B  T  A  G  R  E  A  T  B  A  S  I  N
S  G  K  P  S  S  Y  R  I  A  N  G  T  C  B
G  O  A  R  A  E  S  O  N  O  R  A  N  A  O
C  B  R  I  D  T  O  N  A  A  K  A  K  G  L
H  I  A  V  M  R  A  U  A  L  N  A  H  S  S
I  A  K  A  A  U  A  G  A  H  L  R  L  T  O
H  S  U  K  T  R  K  M  O  A  S  S  O  N  N
U  I  M  R  A  S  A  L  H  N  A  A  U  A  D
A  M  G  H  C  K  T  A  Y  O  I  B  L  N  E
H  P  A  N  A  A  R  U  R  Z  I  A  D  A  M
U  S  R  N  M  I  A  D  R  A  Y  L  N  M  A
A  O  V  N  A  B  O  A  N  T  L  K  U  I  P
N  N  G  A  A  S  A  R  A  B  I  A  N  B  I
I  T  B  E  T  P  A  K  D  A  L  A  Y  M  M
A  I  R  O  T  C  I  V  T  A  E  R  G  A  I
```

DESERTS

ALASHAN	GREAT VICTORIA	PATAGONIAN
ARABIAN	KALAHARI	SAHARA
ATACAMA	KARAKUM	SIMPSON
BETPAK-DALA	KAVIR	SONORAN
BOLSON DE MAPIMI	KYZYLKUM	STURT
CHIHUAHUAN	NAMIB	SYRIAN
GOBI	NUBIAN	TAKLAMAKAN
GREAT BASIN	ORDOS	THAR

D	R	A	O	B	P	U	C	C	U	R	G	U	R	K
E	C	N	O	T	U	F	E	A	N	E	D	U	I	I
L	H	R	H	R	M	D	B	B	A	E	N	M	E	T
B	E	A	U	I	A	E	O	I	M	T	I	O	E	C
A	S	O	R	A	H	A	R	N	O	T	L	F	U	H
T	T	R	R	H	I	S	D	E	T	E	B	R	A	E
R	O	E	I	C	G	Y	R	T	T	S	T	E	L	N
R	F	N	A	G	H	C	A	A	O	A	E	A	D	C
S	D	I	H	N	C	H	W	N	I	B	M	N	F	H
E	R	L	C	I	H	A	L	N	E	P	B	R	S	A
R	A	C	M	K	A	I	L	A	C	A	F	O	S	I
I	W	E	R	C	I	R	N	O	K	C	O	L	C	R
F	E	R	A	O	R	B	U	T	E	P	R	A	C	H
C	R	L	N	R	A	C	P	A	I	N	T	I	N	G
R	S	T	R	G	H	F	O	O	T	S	T	O	O	L

HOUSEHOLD FURNITURE

ARMCHAIR
BEANBAG
BED
BLIND
CABINET
CARPET
CHEST OF DRAWERS
CLOCK
COUCH
CUPBOARD

CURTAIN
EASY CHAIR
FIRE
FOOTSTOOL
FUTON
HIGH CHAIR
KITCHEN CHAIR
LAMP
MIRROR
OTTOMAN

PAINTING
RECLINER
ROCKING CHAIR
RUG
SETTEE
SOFA
TABLE
WARDROBE

Y	E	E	A	A	U	T	O	M	A	T	A	T	N	E
E	A	F	D	E	L	L	I	V	E	D	R	B	A	E
D	R	F	T	S	I	P	Y	T	K	K	O	Q	A	N
O	P	A	L	W	D	S	W	I	L	L	O	W	R	E
C	H	C	B	D	C	Y	D	N	C	O	F	E	O	E
K	O	E	N	R	L	M	O	I	T	F	E	H	T	N
E	N	D	U	R	A	N	C	E	N	S	R	D	A	S
D	E	V	A	D	A	C	I	S	T	N	R	O	R	H
T	T	E	E	N	E	N	A	T	E	I	O	A	I	R
H	Y	U	M	M	Y	D	T	D	A	K	C	D	P	I
O	W	A	L	L	O	W	A	E	A	I	K	A	S	N
U	R	E	O	C	C	U	R	E	N	B	E	M	E	E
G	N	I	L	S	O	G	R	Y	R	N	R	R	R	G
H	E	R	U	S	O	L	C	N	E	D	A	A	R	S
T	N	A	R	Y	T	R	D	E	T	U	L	I	D	O

MATCHING FIRST AND LAST LETTERS

ABRACADABRA
ANTENNA
ARMADA
AUTOMATA
CYNIC
DEVILLED
DILUTED
DOCKED
DREADED
EARPHONE

EFFACE
ENCLOSURE
ENDURANCE
ENSHRINE
GOSLING
KINSFOLK
REOCCUR
RESPIRATOR
ROCKER
ROOFER

THEFT
THOUGHT
TINIEST
TYPIST
TYRANT
WALLOW
WILLOW
YEARLY
YUMMY

```
T Y R K D A T I P O R I T K T
S A Y S P A N A K O P I T A D
L G E T L N K O E O P A T A S
A K N A S O F O R A A O A L A
P E O R T R A A S Y M R A I V
A F H A R A S L K A G T A O A
S T S M A K O O T A E N T E L
T E O A P A L O Z F S D P V K
I T U S A M A S K U K S T I A
T H V A T O K E A A O M U L B
S E L L S L I I S T E V U O Y
I S A A A E A A T S I M E Y M
O O K T D M U D O L M A D E S
I N I A A U I K I Z T A Z T Z
B R I A M I I R A M A L A K S
```

GREEK CUISINE

BAKLAVA
BRIAMI
DAKOS
DOLMADES
FASOLAKIA
FETA
GYRO
HONEY

KALAMARI
KEFTETHES
MELOMAKARONA
MOUSSAKA
OLIVE OIL
OUZO
PASTITSIO
SOUVLAKI

SPANAKOPITA
STRAPATSADA
TARAMASALATA
TIROPITA
TOMATO
TZATZIKI
YEMISTA
YOUVETSI

MAGAZINES

ELLE
ESQUIRE
FHM
FORBES
FORTUNE
GLAMOUR

GRAZIA
MARIE CLAIRE
MAXIM
POPULAR SCIENCE
READERS DIGEST
ROLLING STONE

SHE
THE WEEK
TIME
VANITY FAIR
VOGUE
WIRED

O	P	D	I	U	I	N	W	O	R	D	Y	D	E	D
P	E	R	I	P	H	R	A	S	T	I	C	R	V	S
R	Y	A	A	I	G	N	I	L	B	B	A	B	I	U
X	E	G	S	T	E	L	B	U	L	O	V	E	T	O
I	S	O	I	B	I	S	A	Y	G	S	I	V	A	L
L	U	S	L	M	R	N	S	S	C	P	M	I	K	U
O	F	S	G	R	R	S	G	P	L	O	E	S	L	R
R	F	I	I	S	A	O	R	E	U	Y	S	U	A	R
P	I	P	T	G	C	A	O	T	G	B	O	F	T	A
H	D	Y	G	H	T	N	H	B	N	B	B	F	F	G
O	I	X	A	T	A	Y	L	A	I	A	R	E	O	G
O	B	T	L	S	I	F	F	D	H	G	E	T	G	S
I	T	I	T	Y	D	N	I	W	S	L	V	Y	A	I
Y	N	I	S	U	O	I	C	A	U	Q	O	L	E	F
G	C	U	D	E	D	N	I	W	G	N	O	L	I	U

A LOT TO SAY

BABBLING
CHATTY
DIFFUSE
EFFUSIVE
GABBY
GARRULOUS
GASSY
GOSSIPY

GUSHING
LONG-WINDED
LOQUACIOUS
MOUTHY
PERIPHRASTIC
PLEONASTIC
PRATING
PRATTLING

PROLIX
TALKATIVE
VERBOSE
VOLUBLE
WINDY
WORDY

L	O	R	D	L	A	M	B	O	U	R	N	E	L	E
D	R	B	U	Z	L	U	T	B	I	G	I	E	N	T
N	E	R	G	Z	E	M	P	I	R	E	N	P	A	T
E	I	A	M	A	E	F	O	A	O	R	A	S	I	E
N	D	E	G	J	U	Y	N	E	E	P	L	P	D	N
I	A	B	T	J	J	N	R	K	L	R	A	A	I	I
P	N	U	I	S	Y	P	S	E	A	S	G	R	R	B
S	E	R	H	S	L	D	L	M	V	X	T	T	E	U
I	R	N	M	S	A	O	L	C	N	O	S	A	M	R
R	G	I	L	E	S	R	H	M	P	C	C	N	R	E
C	T	A	M	H	O	N	E	Y	C	R	I	S	P	E
H	H	H	S	E	N	S	Y	D	A	L	K	N	I	P
N	S	G	R	E	E	N	S	L	E	E	V	E	S	D
A	T	P	I	P	P	I	N	Y	E	L	M	A	R	B
B	N	L	A	X	T	O	N	S	S	U	P	E	R	B

APPLE VARIETIES

ASHMEAD'S KERNEL
BRAEBURN
BRAMLEY
COX
CRISPIN
DISCOVERY
ELSTAR
EMPIRE

FUJI
GALA
GRANNY SMITH
GREENSLEEVES
GRENADIER
HOLSTEIN
HONEYCRISP
JAZZ

LAXTON'S SUPERB
LORD LAMBOURNE
MERIDIAN
PINK LADY
PIPPIN
RUBINETTE
SPARTAN

REALLY CLEAN

ASEPTIC
CLEANSED
FAULTLESS
FLAWLESS
FRESH
HYGIENIC
LAUNDERED
PERFECT

PURE
PURIFIED
SANITARY
SPECKLESS
SPOTLESS
STERILE
STERILIZED
UNBLEMISHED

UNCONTAMINATED
UNSOILED
UNSPOTTED
UNSTAINED
UNSULLIED
WASHED

ALL KINDS OF FISH

ANGLERFISH	GOURAMI	POLLACK
BARB	GROUPER	REEDFISH
BICHIR	HADDOCK	SALMON
BONITO	MONKFISH	SNAPPER
CARP	NOTHO	SOLE
CATFISH	PANAQUE	SPILO
CICHLID	PANFISH	TETRA
DANIO	PANGASIUS	TUNA
FLOUNDER	PERCH	WHITEBAIT
GOLDFISH	PLAICE	WRASSE

R	R	E	L	B	R	A	W	E	G	D	E	S	T	R
T	L	D	I	D	R	I	B	K	C	A	L	B	O	H
P	W	R	A	O	G	N	I	L	B	M	A	R	B	C
I	O	N	T	R	S	T	A	R	L	I	N	G	O	N
G	O	I	G	A	N	R	F	W	J	W	K	O	H	I
E	D	B	A	V	K	I	R	I	O	A	K	L	C	F
O	P	O	W	E	E	E	T	R	W	C	Y	K	N	F
N	E	R	O	N	N	V	C	R	U	S	E	R	I	A
K	C	O	N	N	U	D	O	C	A	H	I	A	F	H
T	K	H	O	O	P	O	E	D	H	M	P	L	L	C
E	E	E	K	I	R	H	S	W	E	K	G	Y	L	S
N	R	A	L	L	E	N	U	R	P	O	A	K	U	G
N	E	N	T	H	S	U	R	H	T	O	M	S	B	E
I	H	E	D	G	E	S	P	A	R	R	O	W	P	S
L	T	I	T	L	A	R	K	S	W	A	L	L	O	W

BIRDS

BLACKBIRD	JAY	SHRIKE
BRAMBLING	LINNET	SKYLARK
BULLFINCH	MAGPIE	STARLING
CHAFFINCH	MARTIN	SWALLOW
CROW	PIGEON	SWIFT
CUCKOO	PRUNELLA	THRUSH
DOVE	RAVEN	TITLARK
DUNNOCK	ROBIN	WAGTAIL
HEDGE SPARROW	ROOK	WOODPECKER
HOOPOE	SEDGE WARBLER	WREN

R	A	O	R	G	E	R	B	E	R	A	L	L	C	N
A	I	O	R	E	W	O	L	F	N	R	O	C	A	O
A	N	D	O	R	N	E	D	L	O	G	S	T	R	I
E	O	C	R	N	R	M	D	L	A	D	I	U	N	L
P	G	R	E	A	M	C	E	I	I	D	L	L	A	E
T	E	I	W	L	R	A	O	S	H	L	L	I	T	D
E	B	O	O	I	E	M	R	N	O	C	Y	P	I	N
E	L	T	L	D	W	P	E	A	Y	R	R	S	O	A
W	I	E	F	O	O	A	V	I	N	S	A	O	N	D
S	L	L	N	F	L	N	O	S	O	I	M	T	A	S
L	A	O	U	F	F	U	L	E	E	R	A	Z	Y	T
A	C	I	S	A	L	L	C	E	P	I	A	S	W	O
V	D	V	D	D	L	A	U	R	E	L	I	V	S	C
P	O	P	P	Y	A	R	S	F	E	A	L	A	O	K
R	E	T	S	A	W	G	L	A	D	I	O	L	U	S

FLOWERS

AMARYLLIS	DANDELION	POPPY
ASTER	FREESIA	ROSE
AZALEA	GERBERA	STOCK
BEGONIA	GLADIOLUS	SUNFLOWER
CAMPANULA	GOLDENROD	SWEET PEA
CARNATION	IRIS	TULIP
CLOVER	LILAC	VIOLET
CORNFLOWER	LILY	WALLFLOWER
DAFFODIL	ORCHID	
DAISY	PEONY	

S	D	E	S	I	V	D	A	L	L	I	P	V	T	D
R	I	D	I	C	U	L	O	U	S	U	M	N	I	E
S	I	M	P	L	E	M	I	N	D	E	D	N	U	R
H	A	L	F	W	I	T	T	E	D	E	S	U	N	E
I	I	G	N	O	R	A	N	T	K	A	N	I	R	D
E	V	S	D	O	E	I	I	A	N	W	A	C	E	I
A	A	I	S	R	I	N	B	E	I	I	I	S	A	S
O	C	L	C	N	U	F	A	S	C	L	V	U	S	N
R	U	L	T	I	L	S	E	N	I	M	S	O	O	O
Y	O	Y	I	A	T	H	B	C	I	O	T	R	N	C
Z	U	A	H	D	N	O	E	A	S	R	U	C	A	L
A	S	L	R	U	M	B	I	L	V	O	P	I	B	L
R	M	A	D	U	M	E	T	D	P	N	I	D	L	I
C	D	B	C	I	N	E	P	T	I	I	D	U	E	A
W	P	O	I	N	T	L	E	S	S	C	D	L	F	E

NOT VERY CLEVER

ABSURD
CRAZY
HALF-BAKED
HALF-WITTED
IDIOTIC
IGNORANT
ILL-ADVISED
ILL-CONSIDERED

IMBECILIC
INANE
INEPT
INSANE
LUDICROUS
MAD
MORONIC
POINTLESS

RIDICULOUS
SILLY
SIMPLE-MINDED
STUPID
UNREASONABLE
UNWISE
VACUOUS

A	E	R	O	S	E	A	I	S	H	C	U	F	F	C
A	P	B	N	A	S	A	M	E	T	H	Y	S	T	A
I	D	R	O	N	N	A	I	N	D	I	G	O	D	C
M	L	E	I	N	I	N	B	C	A	L	I	L	R	E
N	O	S	R	C	Y	R	E	S	I	L	V	E	R	G
O	G	E	E	A	O	E	N	I	M	R	A	C	H	G
O	E	P	N	S	G	T	E	R	S	M	A	L	R	S
R	V	I	G	N	E	G	A	V	O	C	A	D	O	H
A	I	A	A	M	A	Q	U	A	M	A	R	I	N	E
M	L	R	P	B	R	A	S	S	A	M	B	E	R	L
E	O	A	M	E	L	I	A	Z	U	R	E	I	A	L
M	R	N	A	U	C	A	B	H	L	G	R	E	E	N
I	A	A	H	L	E	S	I	O	U	Q	R	U	T	R
L	E	Y	C	B	S	C	A	R	L	E	T	C	Q	O
A	M	C	E	N	I	R	A	M	A	R	T	L	U	B

MANY HUES

AMBER	CREAM	MAROON
AMETHYST	CYAN	OLIVE
APRICOT	EBONY	ORANGE
AQUAMARINE	EGGSHELL	ROSE
AVOCADO	FUCHSIA	SCARLET
AZURE	GOLD	SEPIA
BLUE	GREEN	SIENNA
BRASS	INDIGO	SILVER
CARMINE	LILAC	TURQUOISE
CHAMPAGNE	LIME	ULTRAMARINE

I	S	A	I	E	L	O	U	E	D	F	I	T	E	S
G	T	T	Z	M	O	R	A	N	E	T	G	S	T	A
T	I	Z	I	O	U	Z	O	U	E	U	I	A	L	A
O	S	M	L	T	H	S	G	R	E	A	A	K	I	I
U	E	E	L	L	R	I	A	L	M	L	D	A	S	N
A	B	N	I	E	L	I	M	A	I	I	J	A	M	D
R	B	A	I	M	T	A	A	F	L	E	J	D	E	E
G	A	G	M	C	T	N	G	L	B	P	R	I	S	F
L	L	A	A	E	R	I	I	H	B	A	S	L	S	L
A	E	T	R	N	F	L	I	A	O	A	L	B	I	A
R	B	S	A	J	I	J	E	L	I	U	T	C	T	E
I	I	O	C	G	H	A	R	D	A	I	A	N	M	D
U	D	M	S	E	L	B	A	Y	A	D	H	T	A	E
O	I	M	A	T	E	B	E	S	S	A	L	I	S	M
B	S	D	M	T	A	B	O	U	M	E	R	D	E	S

PROVINCES OF ALGERIA

AIN DEFLA	GHARDAIA	ORAN
ALGIERS	GUELMA	OUARGLA
BATNA	ILLIZI	SAIDA
BEJAIA	JIJEL	SETIF
BLIDA	LAGHOUAT	SIDI BEL ABBES
BOUIRA	MASCARA	TEBESSA
BOUMERDES	MEDEA	TIARET
DJELFA	MOSTAGANEM	TISSEMSILT
EL BAYADH	M'SILA	TIZI OUZOU
EL OUED	NAAMA	TLEMCEN

M	M	I	E	A	N	S	Q	C	O	Y	O	T	E	N
N	A	U	N	N	H	I	W	U	A	J	M	A	U	O
U	N	O	A	A	I	N	S	E	I	N	T	I	C	I
K	G	B	C	I	K	P	A	A	H	N	O	J	E	U
A	R	I	I	O	E	A	A	R	C	S	O	E	B	I
R	O	R	R	U	A	E	Y	R	I	C	A	A	R	A
O	V	A	R	Q	A	E	N	A	R	P	O	C	A	Y
N	E	C	U	E	N	E	T	C	K	E	I	M	B	A
A	P	T	H	S	O	T	A	I	N	U	T	E	P	P
C	O	O	L	U	O	A	R	O	E	U	A	H	P	A
M	T	L	L	P	C	N	K	A	S	S	P	U	E	P
A	A	E	A	Y	C	A	S	O	O	I	I	S	C	N
C	T	C	M	O	A	M	U	E	O	A	R	K	A	E
A	O	O	A	C	R	E	M	N	M	P	A	Y	N	E
W	H	S	A	U	Q	S	N	A	C	U	O	T	A	O

WORDS OF NATIVE AMERICAN ORIGIN

ANORAK	LLAMA	PETUNIA
BARBECUE	MACAW	PIRANHA
CANOE	MANATEE	POTATO
CARIBOU	MANGROVE	QUINOA
CASHEW	MOCCASIN	RACCOON
COYOTE	MOOSE	SEQUOIA
COYPU	MUSKRAT	SQUASH
HURRICANE	OCELOT	TAPIR
HUSKY	PAPAYA	TERRAPIN
KAYAK	PECAN	TOUCAN

BOY BANDS

BACKSTREET BOYS
BOYZ II MEN
DRU HILL
HANSON
JACKSON FIVE
JONAS BROTHERS
MIDNIGHT RED

NEW EDITION
NO MERCY
NSYNC
N-TOON
ONE STEP AWAY
OSMONDS
O-TOWN

PLUS ONE
REEL TIGHT
SHAI
THE BOYS
TROOP
TRUE VIBE

C	N	I	A	I	C	I	T	C	R	A	E	A	T	H
T	O	N	A	H	N	U	M	B	I	N	G	M	S	Y
E	L	D	I	T	G	N	I	T	I	B	G	G	I	R
S	R	L	I	C	E	C	O	L	D	I	R	N	B	R
N	L	A	Z	F	R	O	S	T	Y	G	R	O	E	I
Y	N	N	W	E	H	C	U	T	T	I	N	G	R	U
U	N	H	E	A	T	E	D	N	Y	R	T	N	I	W
U	A	O	R	I	L	L	E	T	I	N	R	S	A	C
H	S	E	R	F	Y	A	E	I	E	A	I	F	N	E
C	B	D	I	A	R	T	I	E	L	K	Y	R	N	L
I	I	I	Y	N	E	C	K	C	R	A	L	O	P	C
E	T	G	C	R	V	Y	K	T	A	T	F	Z	A	E
K	T	I	I	I	C	K	A	E	L	B	E	U	N
C	E	R	I	I	H	C	L	O	O	C	G	N	B	R
A	R	F	N	I	S	R	G	N	I	Z	E	E	R	F

DEFINITELY NOT WARM

ARCTIC	FRESH	NUMBING
BITING	FRIGID	POLAR
BITTER	FROSTY	RAW
BLEAK	FROZEN	RIME
CHILLY	GLACIAL	SHIVERY
COOL	ICE-COLD	SIBERIAN
CUTTING	ICY	UNHEATED
FREEZING	KEEN	WINTRY

VISION TEST

APPOINTMENT
BLURRY
CLOSE
DARK
EYESIGHT
FAR
FOCAL DISTANCE
FOCUSED

FOGGY
GLASSES
INVISIBLE
IRIS
LENS COATING
LENSES
LETTERS
LIGHT

NEAR
NUMBERS
PUPIL
ROTATION
SHAPES
SHARP
TWENTY-TWENTY

T	O	A	C	O	O	L	A	L	E	E	N	B	R	C
L	E	R	I	H	S	P	O	R	H	S	O	N	O	N
S	E	N	U	A	C	A	L	G	F	L	R	O	N	O
O	S	H	N	L	O	C	N	I	L	R	F	L	D	R
U	W	O	N	L	L	A	N	W	E	N	O	G	A	T
T	L	E	U	R	O	U	G	H	F	E	L	L	R	H
H	M	K	N	T	Y	E	N	K	R	O	K	P	L	R
D	O	A	L	S	H	E	B	T	K	B	H	E	L	O
E	W	C	H	O	L	D	R	O	F	X	O	R	I	N
V	Y	A	O	S	F	E	O	O	R	O	R	E	H	A
O	L	O	N	K	A	F	Y	W	N	E	N	N	O	L
N	O	N	I	R	E	M	U	D	N	Y	R	D	I	D
N	A	R	A	G	O	N	E	S	A	Y	E	A	W	S
E	P	O	R	T	L	A	N	D	O	L	O	L	Y	A
R	H	E	B	R	I	D	E	A	N	D	E	E	L	Y

BREEDS OF SHEEP

ARAGONESA
BORERAY
COOLALEE
HEBRIDEAN
HILL RADNOR
LACAUNE
LINCOLN
LLANWENOG
LLEYN

LONK
MASHAM
MERINO
NORFOLK HORN
NORTH RONALDSAY
ORKNEY
OXFORD
PERENDALE
PORTLAND

ROUGH FELL
SHROPSHIRE
SOAY
SOUTH DEVON
SOUTHDOWN
SUFFOLK
WENSLEYDALE

S	Y	A	J	E	U	L	B	X	S	R	E	G	I	T
R	O	C	K	I	E	S	A	O	E	S	S	C	L	T
R	S	S	L	E	G	N	A	S	T	Y	B	E	W	R
E	S	R	E	G	D	O	D	E	A	A	X	I	E	S
D	I	O	M	I	W	A	I	T	R	R	N	S	N	L
S	S	E	V	A	R	B	T	I	I	S	B	A	E	A
O	S	S	L	P	R	A	E	H	P	U	T	S	P	N
X	N	L	R	I	H	I	N	W	C	H	S	O	A	I
G	I	A	N	T	S	I	N	G	L	L	G	R	D	D
S	L	N	S	O	R	N	L	E	E	L	N	T	R	R
M	R	O	N	L	I	N	T	L	R	R	B	S	E	A
E	A	I	S	N	A	I	D	N	I	S	S	A	S	C
T	M	T	R	R	C	Y	A	B	R	E	W	E	R	S
S	D	A	P	S	R	H	O	S	T	A	S	R	E	I
Y	A	N	K	E	E	S	O	R	I	O	L	E	S	S

MLB TEAMS

ANGELS	INDIANS	RAYS
ASTROS	MARINERS	RED SOX
ATHLETICS	MARLINS	ROCKIES
BLUE JAYS	METS	ROYALS
BRAVES	NATIONALS	TIGERS
BREWERS	ORIOLES	TWINS
CARDINALS	PADRES	WHITE SOX
CUBS	PHILLIES	YANKEES
DODGERS	PIRATES	
GIANTS	RANGERS	

S	L	L	U	B	A	S	T	E	N	R	O	H	R	Z
S	E	L	S	R	U	P	S	G	N	O	T	K	M	G
S	R	E	P	P	I	L	C	S	K	B	R	B	A	K
R	O	C	K	E	T	S	K	S	S	W	A	S	V	S
P	A	C	E	R	S	W	E	W	G	H	I	T	E	K
I	R	S	N	S	A	I	A	W	N	E	L	E	R	C
S	A	N	Z	H	L	R	I	S	I	A	B	G	I	U
T	P	U	I	Z	R	Z	R	P	K	T	L	G	C	B
O	T	S	Z	I	A	E	I	R	C	E	A	U	K	S
N	O	I	O	R	I	J	E	I	K	M	Z	N	S	K
S	R	R	D	L	S	N	A	C	I	L	E	P	R	C
G	S	S	A	R	E	D	N	U	H	T	R	E	E	I
S	O	V	L	C	E	L	T	I	C	S	S	R	L	N
P	A	D	S	R	E	K	A	L	V	E	L	M	S	K
C	R	S	E	V	L	O	W	R	E	B	M	I	T	A

NBA TEAMS

BUCKS
BULLS
CAVALIERS
CELTICS
CLIPPERS
GRIZZLIES
HAWKS
HEAT
HORNETS
JAZZ

KINGS
KNICKS
LAKERS
MAGIC
MAVERICKS
NUGGETS
PACERS
PELICANS
PISTONS
RAPTORS

ROCKETS
SPURS
SUNS
THUNDER
TIMBERWOLVES
TRAIL BLAZERS
WARRIORS
WIZARDS

G	A	L	G	A	B	S	T	R	E	S	S	E	D	R
N	U	S	I	S	T	D	R	B	T	R	S	L	S	G
A	N	A	O	N	D	E	E	G	P	D	R	E	M	A
T	T	G	U	A	V	V	R	D	S	L	E	O	P	P
S	I	B	A	I	P	I	D	R	S	O	U	E	O	B
E	I	N	L	R	S	L	E	R	P	U	P	G	P	D
I	B	E	U	I	E	I	D	N	Y	R	N	I	S	S
L	D	U	E	E	N	M	I	N	E	D	N	G	A	E
U	Y	G	S	E	M	B	A	L	N	O	P	D	W	T
U	N	D	D	R	S	T	L	Y	O	A	P	I	U	O
O	S	I	U	N	G	D	E	N	R	I	R	B	T	T
A	T	P	P	B	A	E	E	G	E	O	E	A	R	R
G	P	E	S	S	G	I	K	R	T	D	A	N	O	A
W	E	T	S	E	A	L	G	O	O	R	O	O	M	P
T	E	R	L	U	A	E	R	T	M	M	I	D	R	O

ALSO A WORD WHEN REVERSED

ARE	GNAT	ROOM
BAG	LEEK	ROTOR
BIN	LIVED	SAG
BUD	MAY	SAW
BUN	MID	SPEED
BUS	NOON	SPIN
DEBUT	PART	STEW
DELIVER	PEP	STRESSED
DENIM	PLUG	SUNG
DOOR	REINED	TIN

T	F	U	L	G	U	R	I	T	E	P	F	P	M	U
E	X	N	A	I	D	I	S	B	O	L	I	Q	I	O
K	E	K	V	O	L	C	A	N	I	C	T	T	L	P
T	L	N	S	Z	S	R	E	N	I	E	C	D	L	A
I	I	W	T	I	T	E	T	L	E	N	A	E	E	L
T	S	O	A	E	U	R	S	A	S	I	S	B	F	I
E	E	R	I	O	S	U	A	P	T	R	E	O	I	N
P	U	C	N	R	S	M	P	U	C	U	K	T	O	E
L	Q	X	E	R	Y	P	A	C	Q	T	O	T	R	N
A	I	Y	D	T	S	N	U	L	D	N	O	L	I	M
T	L	R	A	P	N	L	G	T	T	E	R	E	U	I
E	A	O	U	L	L	G	U	U	B	V	C	A	L	E
N	L	N	L	E	S	C	L	P	A	A	M	I	L	K
F	E	C	T	Y	N	A	F	F	I	T	E	N	O	R
E	T	I	L	R	E	P	Z	C	R	Y	S	T	A	L

GLASS

AVENTURINE	FULGURITE	PYREX
BOTTLE	LALIQUE	QUARTZ
CROOKES	MILK	SILEX
CROWN	MILLEFIORI	SMALT
CRYSTAL	OBSIDIAN	SPUN
CULLET	OPALINE	STAINED
CUT	PASTE	TEKTITE
FLINT	PERLITE	TIFFANY
FLOAT	PLATE	VOLCANIC

K	N	E	B	U	T	U	A	L	U	T	A	P	S	E
B	S	I	N	E	R	O	T	A	C	C	I	S	E	D
R	U	A	B	P	A	T	R	E	D	N	I	L	Y	C
E	T	N	L	E	C	K	S	S	L	I	D	E	D	K
B	R	F	S	F	L	R	E	T	T	I	N	R	R	S
U	I	I	H	E	C	L	U	R	I	A	C	L	O	A
T	P	L	S	V	N	I	J	C	A	R	N	E	P	L
G	O	T	I	A	E	B	R	A	I	T	R	D	P	F
N	D	E	D	L	T	E	U	T	R	B	R	E	E	R
I	T	R	I	C	T	E	B	R	E	E	L	O	R	E
L	R	P	R	O	E	L	E	C	N	M	N	E	M	T
I	O	A	T	T	R	T	I	L	R	E	U	S	I	L
O	T	P	E	U	U	S	C	A	S	M	R	L	R	I
B	E	E	P	A	B	E	T	M	R	A	R	I	O	F
T	R	R	G	I	R	P	I	P	E	T	T	E	E	V

LABORATORY APPARATUS

AUTOCLAVE	DESICCATOR	SLIDE
BEAKER	DROPPER	SPATULA
BELL JAR	FILTER FLASK	STAND
BOILING TUBE	FILTER PAPER	STIRRER
BUNSEN BURNER	MORTAR	TRIPOD
BURETTE	PESTLE	U-TUBE
CLAMP	PETRI DISH	VOLUMETRIC FLASK
CRUCIBLE	PIPETTE	
CYLINDER	RETORT	

A	G	E	E	D	I	S	Y	R	T	N	U	O	C	C
H	N	K	P	U	B	S	N	T	Y	P	I	E	R	S
O	I	C	S	L	S	O	Y	I	L	B	E	I	K	E
I	S	G	O	L	E	N	R	E	A	S	G	E	E	L
N	S	S	H	C	I	P	A	K	L	T	E	U	H	T
O	O	G	E	L	N	D	R	L	N	L	N	O	R	S
S	T	I	B	S	A	S	O	E	C	E	A	U	V	A
N	R	A	R	R	T	N	N	F	C	C	Y	V	O	C
A	E	N	I	E	R	S	D	O	F	H	C	S	N	M
K	B	D	D	V	A	I	E	S	W	A	A	E	A	D
E	A	U	E	O	T	G	U	I	T	D	D	U	R	E
S	C	B	S	L	H	G	R	D	R	I	O	U	N	C
P	S	H	E	C	S	A	O	U	D	P	I	N	O	S
C	E	L	T	I	C	H	S	R	E	D	H	A	I	R
C	E	I	S	M	R	A	F	E	S	T	L	I	K	A

SCOTLAND, IRELAND AND WALES

CABER TOSSING
CASTLES
CELTIC
CELTS
CLANS
CLOVER
COAL
COUNTRYSIDE
DAFFODILS
DRUIDS

EURO
FARMS
HAGGIS
HEBRIDES
HIGHLANDS
KILTS
LEEKS
LEPRECHAUNS
MOUNTAINS
NO SNAKES

ORKNEYS
PRIESTS
PUBS
RED HAIR
RUGBY
SGIAN DUBH
SHEEP
SNOWDONIA
TARTAN
VALLEYS

V	N	S	E	C	H	E	N	I	N	B	L	A	N	C
I	E	R	R	E	C	N	A	S	L	E	V	A	T	C
N	A	S	I	V	M	U	S	C	A	D	E	T	E	A
H	D	Y	O	B	E	A	U	J	O	L	A	I	S	V
O	J	L	L	P	M	E	V	O	U	V	R	A	Y	A
V	E	V	E	I	R	B	D	M	T	O	K	A	Y	B
E	R	A	D	E	E	L	E	T	A	C	S	U	M
R	E	N	T	S	V	B	T	O	O	M	A	K	S	D
D	P	E	N	P	A	S	S	E	A	L	C	A	A
E	I	R	A	O	O	J	E	D	I	A	I	O	L	G
A	G	O	M	R	S	U	O	K	O	N	C	H	L	A
S	O	R	E	T	T	C	E	I	T	V	A	E	E	L
T	N	U	R	E	C	A	N	A	R	Y	N	A	C	A
I	W	O	C	R	F	R	A	S	C	A	T	I	U	M
L	E	D	O	R	V	I	E	T	O	G	T	O	B	T

VARIETIES OF WINE

ALICANT
ASTI
BEAUJOLAIS
BEAUNE
BUCELLAS
CANARY
CAVA
CHENIN BLANC
CREMANT DE LOIRE
DAO

DOURO
FRASCATI
HOCK
JEREPIGO
MALAGA
MEDOC
MUSCADET
MUSCATEL
ORVIETO
PIESPORTER

RETSINA
RIOJA
SANCERRE
SEKT
SOAVE
SYLVANER
TAVEL
TOKAY
VINHO VERDE
VOUVRAY

N	O	T	T	U	M	W	S	R	E	T	T	O	R	T
S	A	F	K	E	S	S	N	O	E	G	I	P	B	T
O	I	R	S	L	R	E	G	R	U	B	M	A	H	E
A	O	O	I	R	I	G	R	R	R	E	L	B	A	L
P	O	E	S	T	E	A	K	G	A	H	I	T	C	K
G	R	O	U	S	E	A	U	K	B	E	A	U	I	C
S	A	U	S	A	G	E	E	Q	B	A	T	R	B	U
B	N	O	S	I	N	E	V	A	I	R	X	K	R	N
E	B	A	C	O	N	E	L	N	T	T	O	E	A	K
L	K	M	L	E	K	T	O	N	G	U	E	Y	W	S
O	I	I	R	A	O	C	E	R	A	H	L	P	N	G
S	D	N	A	G	M	A	U	T	B	N	I	A	O	I
S	N	C	G	T	R	B	R	D	D	E	V	T	R	P
I	E	E	T	N	A	S	A	E	H	P	E	E	O	A
R	Y	S	C	H	I	C	K	E	N	R	R	F	A	E

BUTCHER'S COUNTER

BACON
BEEF
BRAWN
CHICKEN
DUCK
GOOSE
GROUSE
HAMBURGER
HARE
HEART

KIDNEY
LAMB
LIVER
MINCE
MUTTON
OXTAIL
PATE
PHEASANT
PIGEON
PIG'S KNUCKLE

PORK
QUAIL
RABBIT
RISSOLE
SAUSAGE
STEAK
TONGUE
TROTTERS
TURKEY
VENISON

```
P O E F S E P O N I A R D S A
I Q B A Y O N E T R A E P S L
K U Q E E K S P R A O S S E E
E A K W A H A M O T C N F T Y
C R E G G A D O T I L I A W P
F T N D W A D E M A N E P E E
A E S R M R L I I K R O D E W
P R G O A I T R E I P A R B E
O S L W T A E I C L I O F P T
R T A S R O W G A G M D A E E
T A I D O O K R U Y E G Y C H
L F V A B L R R A O N R P N C
A F E O N O T L I A V E E A A
C I L R W A C K P D U F W L M
R L L B V E F I N K K C I L F
```

BLADES

ARROW	EPEE	PONIARD
BAYONET	FLICK-KNIFE	QUARTERSTAFF
BOWIE KNIFE	FOIL	RAPIER
BROADSWORD	GLAIVE	SCIMITAR
CALTROP	LANCE	SPEAR
CLAYMORE	MACHETE	STILETTO
DAGGER	PANGA	TOMAHAWK
DIRK	PIKE	VOUGE

```
R  T  I  G  E  O  G  R  A  P  H  Y  A  G  H
Y  I  M  L  Y  Y  G  O  L  O  I  B  G  E  O
A  R  Y  G  O  L  O  E  G  C  S  S  N  O  M
E  Y  O  H  O  I  H  S  E  A  O  P  E  M  E
M  R  B  T  S  Y  A  G  B  L  C  H  N  E  E
A  T  U  E  S  I  E  I  R  C  I  Y  G  T  C
T  S  I  T  L  I  N  M  A  U  A  S  L  R  O
H  I  C  C  A  O  H  A  Y  L  L  I  I  Y  N
E  M  O  L  N  R  G  H  P  U  S  C  S  S  O
M  E  H  B  G  Y  E  Y  T  S  T  S  H  M  M
A  H  T  O  U  M  D  T  M  E  U  I  U  M  I
T  C  L  T  A  G  R  C  I  T  D  S  H  E  C
I  A  A  A  G  C  A  I  O  L  I  C  Y  B  S
C  R  E  N  E  E  M  G  A  C  E  G  G  N
S  T  H  Y  S  T  A  L  M  Y  S  A  C  L  S
```

SCHOOL SUBJECTS

ALGEBRA	GEOGRAPHY	LITERATURE
ART	GEOLOGY	MATHEMATICS
BIOLOGY	GEOMETRY	MUSIC
BOTANY	GYM	PHYSICS
CALCULUS	HEALTH	SOCIAL STUDIES
CHEMISTRY	HISTORY	SPANISH
DRAMA	HOME ECONOMICS	
ENGLISH	LANGUAGES	

E	A	G	E	W	E	E	O	G	R	I	N	D	M	B
D	M	O	S	N	A	D	D	E	I	L	L	O	D	A
I	C	O	K	W	D	L	I	I	P	P	N	G	A	C
L	T	F	P	F	I	O	K	S	L	S	O	O	F	K
S	W	Y	I	A	E	T	V	T	T	S	G	P	F	S
L	I	F	L	K	R	S	C	E	H	N	O	S	Y	I
I	S	O	F	I	I	D	R	H	R	E	O	C	O	D
A	T	O	K	E	C	W	E	B	S	A	D	R	O	E
R	K	T	C	S	A	N	N	F	I	T	U	O	F	C
W	E	D	I	L	S	E	S	O	N	G	A	O	G	F
E	R	K	K	E	L	L	E	Z	A	G	S	N	F	N
V	A	P	R	I	M	O	S	L	I	D	E	P	C	E
R	E	G	U	L	A	R	F	O	O	T	Z	A	I	E
A	C	A	U	E	D	I	L	S	L	I	A	T	D	N
C	A	S	P	E	R	D	I	S	A	S	T	E	R	A

SKATEBOARD TRICKS

BACKSIDE	FRONTSIDE	OLLIE
BIGSPIN	GAZELLE	POGO
CARVE	GOOFY FOOT	PRIMO SLIDE
CASPER DISASTER	GRIND	RAILSLIDE
COCO SLIDE	KICKFLIP	REGULAR FOOT
DAFFY	MCTWIST	SWITCH STANCE
END-OVER	MONSTER WALK	TAILSLIDE
FAKIE	NOSESLIDE	WALK THE DOG

STATES OF BRAZIL

ACRE
ALAGOAS
AMAPA
AMAZONAS
BAHIA
CEARA
DISTRITO FEDERAL
ESPIRITO SANTO

GOIAS
MARANHAO
MINAS GERAIS
PARAIBA
PARANA
PIAUI
RIO DE JANEIRO
RIO GRANDE DO SUL

RONDONIA
RORAIMA
SANTA CATARINA
SAO PAULO
SERGIPE
TOCANTINS

E	Y	E	T	R	E	T	S	E	C	U	O	L	G	E
E	P	O	L	L	E	D	H	E	R	E	F	O	R	D
K	C	A	L	B	H	S	L	E	W	G	N	I	U	L
N	R	O	H	G	N	O	L	H	S	I	L	G	N	E
K	E	G	O	N	R	E	T	X	E	D	L	O	A	O
D	R	N	U	D	E	L	I	O	M	H	S	I	R	I
E	M	A	R	E	N	R	O	H	T	R	O	H	S	W
R	J	K	P	E	R	I	E	R	I	H	S	R	Y	A
N	L	E	E	D	N	X	D	G	R	O	H	S	R
L	N	D	R	R	T	A	S	L	B	A	X	T	A	E
O	N	C	A	S	R	I	N	E	I	Y	E	Y	K	D
C	O	A	E	G	E	Y	H	G	Y	Y	S	C	W	P
N	R	R	H	B	J	Y	L	W	U	I	S	O	J	O
I	N	O	V	E	D	H	T	U	O	S	U	D	D	L
L	R	W	D	N	A	L	H	G	I	H	S	S	H	L

BREEDS OF CATTLE

AYRSHIRE	JERSEY	SHORTHORN
DEXTER	KERRY	SOUTH DEVON
ENGLISH LONGHORN	LINCOLN RED	SUSSEX
GLOUCESTER	LUING	WELSH BLACK
GUERNSEY	POLLED HEREFORD	WHITE PARK
HIGHLAND	RED ANGUS	
IRISH MOILED	RED POLL	

N	R	E	E	S	E	N	A	G	N	A	M	M	Y	H
M	U	I	S	S	A	T	O	P	I	A	B	U	Y	E
M	U	I	H	T	I	L	E	M	T	A	E	I	N	C
M	A	N	T	I	M	O	N	Y	R	R	R	S	E	O
L	U	E	O	N	M	U	I	D	O	S	Y	E	T	P
E	U	I	N	R	O	S	M	C	G	E	L	N	S	P
K	F	M	C	I	I	B	O	M	E	N	L	G	G	E
C	H	E	I	L	D	B	R	Y	N	I	I	A	N	R
I	Y	G	V	A	A	O	B	A	N	C	U	M	U	M
N	D	E	E	L	U	C	I	L	C	O	M	Z	T	U
N	R	L	T	S	U	R	O	H	P	S	O	H	P	I
O	O	G	E	R	M	A	N	I	U	M	O	R	N	D
N	G	K	R	Y	P	T	O	N	D	L	O	G	O	A
E	E	U	C	I	M	U	I	N	A	T	I	T	E	R
X	N	S	N	N	I	S	I	L	I	C	O	N	N	O

ELEMENTS

ANTIMONY	HYDROGEN	NITROGEN
ARSENIC	IODINE	PHOSPHORUS
BERYLLIUM	IRON	POTASSIUM
BROMINE	KRYPTON	RADIUM
CALCIUM	LEAD	SILICON
CARBON	LITHIUM	SILVER
COBALT	MAGNESIUM	SODIUM
COPPER	MANGANESE	TITANIUM
GERMANIUM	NEON	TUNGSTEN
GOLD	NICKEL	XENON

E	S	I	D	E	L	I	N	E	K	I	C	K	C	F
K	K	N	S	O	A	S	T	S	D	H	E	R	W	T
C	D	I	R	S	O	G	B	I	A	E	O	A	O	W
I	R	R	C	L	A	Y	L	R	P	S	G	P	M	O
K	A	L	O	K	L	P	G	T	S	P	A	P	N	H
Y	W	K	U	A	O	E	D	B	O	T	I	S	E	A
T	R	C	T	O	I	U	A	N	E	V	R	N	I	N
L	O	A	N	V	F	R	T	O	A	A	I	A	G	D
A	F	B	I	E	K	R	T	S	D	H	T	D	E	E
N	L	R	O	R	F	I	S	T	P	A	S	S	B	D
E	L	E	P	C	G	K	N	I	W	O	R	H	T	P
P	U	N	D	A	U	O	T	U	V	L	E	R	N	A
D	F	R	U	R	L	L	A	B	E	R	A	U	Q	S
D	L	O	H	R	E	V	O	L	R	T	A	H	E	S
S	O	C	L	Y	F	R	E	E	K	I	C	K	S	I

GAELIC FOOTBALL

CHARGE
CORNERBACK
CROSSBAR
DIVOT
FIST PASS
FOUL
FREE KICK
FULL FORWARD

GOAL
HAND PASS
KICK OUT
OVERCARRY
OVERHOLD
PENALTY KICK
POINT
SIDELINE KICK

SOLO
SQUARE BALL
THROW-IN
TIPPING
TOE-TAP
TWO-HANDED PASS

```
H O D N E K O I A D A P S E R
R A T I M I C S P A D R O O N
T T U L W A R R P S O B L I B
E K I R P A N W K E R E B A S
N E R L E W R E I P A R A S I
O I P E O G F K M O D R E M B
Y D A E G O N D I E N N F A A
A R E G I G V A A N A A I L S
B N T L E C A A H E H R N L S
S E E E O S H D E C K N K S A
L K H D V T S I S S A P K W L
L U C I M A L A B A T I C O T
I K T R S A E S I M A K A R U
B R A K O E L L U A N E J D C
L I H M W D A E G D A K I D S
```

BLADED WEAPONS

ASSEGAI	ESPADA	KUKRI
BAYONET	FOIL	PIKE
BILBO	GLEAVE	RAPIER
BILL	HANGER	SABER
CHIB	HATCHET	SCIMITAR
CUTLASS	JACKKNIFE	SMALL-SWORD
DAGGER	KATANA	SPADROON
DAMASCENE	KENDO	SPEAR
DIRK	KHANDA	TOLEDO
EPEE	KIRPAN	TULWAR

F	L	O	W	R	E	B	M	I	T	O	U	G	E	L
O	S	E	G	G	S	H	E	L	L	X	L	A	C	S
U	E	W	O	E	B	U	T	I	C	A	I	L	O	C
T	T	O	H	A	E	S	O	H	A	L	V	L	J	E
E	I	N	I	I	O	R	A	C	O	F	O	I	A	M
R	H	Y	C	H	T	M	I	N	U	I	R	N	V	E
S	P	X	G	R	P	E	G	E	E	A	Y	A	A	D
P	A	T	A	E	A	E	N	O	B	L	V	N	I	
A	R	S	G	T	M	A	L	L	E	T	N	G	N	U
C	G	N	L	A	T	E	M	N	U	G	M	Y	O	M
E	E	L	L	E	H	S	A	E	S	A	I	N	B	T
W	R	E	M	S	M	O	K	Y	L	S	S	O	R	A
O	G	K	C	A	L	B	H	C	A	E	P	B	A	U
N	E	T	B	R	R	P	R	I	C	H	L	E	C	P
S	J	E	T	A	U	S	B	C	N	E	N	I	L	E

BLACK, WHITE, AND IN-BETWEEN

BONE	GLAUCOUS	ONYX
CARBON	GRAPHITE	OUTER SPACE
CHAMPAGNE	GUNMETAL	PEACH-BLACK
CREAM	IVORY	RICH
EBONY	JET	SEASHELL
ECRU	LINEN	SMOKY
EERIE	MAGNOLIA	SNOW
EGGSHELL	MARS	TIMBER WOLF
FLAX	MEDIUM TAUPE	VANILLA
GHOST	NAVAJO	WHITE

TAKE YOUR TIME

ADJOURNMENT	INTERVAL	REST
BREAK	LULL	STANDSTILL
BREATHING SPACE	PAUSE	STOPPAGE
COMMA	POSTPONEMENT	STRIKE
DEFERMENT	PUTTING-OFF	SUSPENSION
HALT	RECESS	TAKE FIVE
INTERLUDE	REMISSION	WAIT
INTERRUPTION	RESPITE	

```
R E X C O I T E P A T T C L N
W R S A G E J T C S O O E I W
A P I K A I A N O A L T O R O
A N G O R A C I T T A O H R R
L Ü A O L Z K U T I A H S H B
N N R V T A R Q O N L A W I K
B A K S A L A E N L L R O N O
E C Y A N H B L T E I G N E E
L E O A I K B R A U H E S L P
G L H A L R I A I R C N V A M
I B D S R A T H L O N T I N A
A A H U I L M R X P I E E D W
N S S V T L O I R E H R N E S
A R C T I C O P H A C N N R S
E X O F K E H P L N N B A A L
```

BREEDS OF RABBIT AND HARE

ALASKA	FOX	RHINELANDER
ANGORA	HARLEQUIN	ROCK
ARCTIC	HAVANA	SABLE
ARGENTE	HIMALAYAN	SAGE
BELGIAN	HOTOT	SATIN
BROWN	JACKRABBIT	SNOWSHOE
CHINCHILLA	OAR-LOP	SWAMP
COTTONTAIL	PIKA	TAN
DUTCH	POLISH	TAPETI
EUROPEAN	REX	VIENNA

A	V	E	S	S	E	N	O	R	A	B	R	S	L	H
N	G	I	O	C	I	F	I	N	G	A	M	S	A	C
R	Q	R	S	E	I	G	N	I	O	R	S	E	D	A
E	S	S	A	C	R	K	N	I	G	H	T	H	Y	E
G	R	S	O	N	O	E	E	A	R	L	A	C	E	S
A	M	E	E	A	D	U	K	N	V	S	R	U	K	I
W	A	N	P	R	R	S	N	N	A	U	O	D	U	O
O	R	O	S	A	E	U	E	T	U	H	S	D	D	A
D	Q	I	I	E	T	E	O	I	E	J	T	N	D	T
N	U	H	U	E	T	R	P	S	G	S	A	A	N	E
E	E	C	Q	D	M	M	I	E	A	N	S	R	A	N
E	S	R	R	R	A	O	C	F	V	E	G	R	O	
U	S	A	A	U	O	I	D	C	I	I	A	U	G	R
Q	L	M	M	R	E	E	A	I	I	A	L	V	R	A
D	R	O	L	E	G	E	I	L	V	V	N	A	R	B

NOBLES

BARONESS
BARONET
EARL
GRAND DUCHESS
GRAND DUKE
GRAND SEIGNEUR
JUNKER
KNIGHT
LADY

LAIRD
LIEGE LORD
LIFE PEER
MAGNIFICO
MARCHIONESS
MARQUESS
MARQUIS
PATRICIAN
PEERESS

QUEEN DOWAGER
SEIGNIOR
STAROSTA
TAOISEACH
THANE
VAVASOUR
VICOMTE
VIDAME
VISCOUNTESS

A	N	T	I	O	C	H	L	O	E	M	S	S	S	N
A	S	D	E	L	P	H	I	X	A	I	I	O	A	S
A	N	E	C	A	R	H	T	R	M	L	L	X	S	I
A	X	S	N	E	H	T	A	A	O	Y	O	M	U	L
A	N	O	D	O	D	T	L	P	P	S	H	U	S	O
C	A	T	H	C	H	A	A	M	O	P	E	A	S	P
R	R	R	R	O	S	E	P	Y	D	O	L	L	A	I
E	A	O	N	R	N	A	H	T	E	S	L	E	N	R
T	G	Y	B	I	S	T	R	I	S	E	E	X	R	T
E	E	L	O	N	O	A	Y	L	S	I	S	A	A	A
O	M	P	E	T	G	L	G	E	O	D	P	N	C	T
S	E	D	O	H	R	P	I	N	S	O	O	D	I	R
R	H	I	T	H	A	C	A	E	H	N	N	R	L	A
E	S	A	I	D	I	D	Y	M	A	I	T	I	A	P
H	E	R	A	C	L	E	A	A	S	A	L	A	H	S

ANCIENT GREEK MAP

ALEXANDRIA
ANTIOCH
ARGOS
ATHENS
BOEOTIA
CORINTH
CRETE
DELPHI
DIDYMA
DODONA

HALICARNASSUS
HELLESPONT
HERACLEA
ITHACA
MARATHON
MEGARA
MYTILENE
NAXOS
NEAPOLIS
ODESSOS

PHRYGIA
PLATAEA
POSEIDONIA
PYLOS
RHODES
SALAMIS
SPARTA
THRACE
TRIPOLIS
TROY

T	B	N	R	U	O	D	A	P	M	O	P	I	C	E
O	I	N	O	E	N	I	M	R	A	C	P	E	E	D
S	G	S	F	T	I	N	H	R	U	K	F	A	A	A
H	A	N	H	L	N	T	O	H	L	N	U	E	M	I
O	R	N	A	E	A	O	F	A	T	I	C	S	A	F
C	U	I	A	D	L	M	I	B	R	R	H	I	G	R
K	B	E	S	I	N	L	I	T	A	B	S	R	E	E
I	Y	I	C	A	L	A	P	N	A	O	I	E	N	N
N	R	A	H	U	L	U	F	I	G	N	A	C	T	C
G	H	C	A	E	P	M	H	O	N	O	R	S	A	H
P	E	R	S	I	A	N	O	T	U	K	I	A	A	R
T	C	Y	C	L	A	M	E	N	O	A	Y	E	C	O
Y	M	O	S	S	O	L	B	Y	R	R	E	H	C	S
I	N	S	H	R	I	M	P	C	O	R	A	L	S	E
O	O	T	B	H	T	N	A	R	A	M	A	C	I	H

SHADES OF PINK

AMARANTH
BRINK
CARNATION
CERISE
CHERRY BLOSSOM
CORAL
CYCLAMEN
DEEP CARMINE
FANDANGO

FLAMINGO
FRENCH ROSE
FUCHSIA
HOT
MAGENTA
PEACH
PERSIAN
POMPADOUR
PUCE

RUBY
SALMON
SHELL PINK
SHOCKING
SHRIMP
THULIAN
ULTRA

T	F	B	R	D	R	I	V	E	B	E	L	T	E	R
U	U	E	O	S	O	C	F	S	I	L	L	N	X	O
R	E	C	C	E	R	N	H	I	O	E	T	C	H	T
B	L	A	K	L	E	E	T	O	B	E	O	D	A	A
O	I	R	E	A	T	N	S	N	K	N	I	O	U	I
C	N	B	R	E	L	F	A	S	N	E	L	R	S	D
H	J	U	C	S	I	F	A	E	S	E	P	H	T	A
A	E	R	O	L	F	G	C	H	T	U	U	S	V	R
R	C	E	V	I	R	T	L	T	S	A	M	U	A	E
G	T	T	E	O	I	N	A	D	O	K	P	P	L	K
E	O	T	R	N	A	M	L	K	E	R	N	P	V	G
R	R	O	G	F	L	Y	W	H	E	E	L	A	E	M
M	E	R	O	C	K	E	R	A	R	M	M	T	R	T
R	O	I	G	N	I	T	I	O	N	C	O	I	L	C
D	D	L	O	F	I	N	A	M	T	E	L	N	I	I

CAR ENGINE PARTS

AIR FILTER	FLYWHEEL	RADIATOR
CARBURETTOR	FUEL INJECTOR	ROCKER ARM
CHOKE	GASKET	ROCKER COVER
CONNECTING ROD	IGNITION COIL	SUMP
CRANKSHAFT	INLET MANIFOLD	TAPPET
DRIVE BELT	OIL PUMP	TURBOCHARGER
EXHAUST VALVE	OIL SEAL	
FAN BELT	PUSHROD	

S	U	M	T	I	L	I	C	L	N	H	C	E	R	R
E	C	N	W	O	R	C	C	W	T	A	P	H	L	R
T	A	G	N	M	Y	G	O	V	R	O	M	E	L	B
T	R	N	T	A	A	R	E	B	B	D	L	L	E	E
E	T	I	F	P	B	N	O	R	P	R	N	L	T	A
R	R	C	A	H	A	N	I	B	E	G	A	O	A	U
A	I	A	R	R	O	R	P	L	O	T	N	P	I	B
G	D	R	K	I	C	A	C	T	A	N	L	O	R	D
I	G	T	N	R	P	L	S	H	E	R	D	I	C	I
C	E	D	E	Y	F	H	G	T	M	U	T	T	F	A
W	I	P	R	R	E	I	O	R	A	E	S	G	E	L
A	E	U	G	E	P	X	L	L	A	C	N	S	C	I
I	S	R	T	A	S	H	A	E	M	P	C	T	I	D
M	U	L	L	E	V	G	R	M	I	E	H	E	R	T
M	R	R	F	O	O	R	P	E	S	A	E	R	G	T

PAPERS

BALLOT
BOND
BROWN
CARBON
CARTRIDGE
CIGARETTE
CREPE
CROWN
EXAM

FILE
FILTER
GRAPH
GREASEPROOF
INDIA
KRAFT
LAID
LITMUS
MANILA

NOTE
PAPYRUS
PARCHMENT
RICE
SHEET
TISSUE
TRACING
VELLUM

C	O	R	R	U	P	T	I	O	N	F	G	A	G	N
O	N	E	F	P	O	A	C	H	I	N	G	G	O	A
U	O	D	S	R	I	B	T	R	I	K	N	S	D	P
N	I	I	A	L	A	H	L	K	G	I	R	T	R	I
T	T	C	B	S	E	U	L	A	T	A	N	V	I	R
E	R	I	O	F	A	A	D	F	C	A	I	A	N	A
R	O	M	T	D	T	M	I	M	Y	K	K	N	K	C
F	T	O	A	S	B	L	Z	S	R	Y	M	D	D	Y
E	X	H	G	Y	P	T	F	I	E	R	G	A	R	R
I	E	T	E	O	R	O	A	R	B	E	N	L	I	A
T	K	I	H	E	R	U	A	O	B	T	I	I	V	L
I	R	S	A	G	S	F	J	R	O	T	G	S	I	G
N	I	S	E	E	S	J	B	R	R	A	G	M	N	R
G	O	R	E	D	R	U	M	E	E	B	U	U	G	U
N	Y	N	E	C	R	A	L	T	L	P	M	S	S	B

CRIMES

ARSON
BATTERY
BLACKMAIL
BURGLARY
CORRUPTION
COUNTERFEITING
DRINK-DRIVING
EXTORTION
FORGERY

FRAUD
HOMICIDE
LARCENY
MUGGING
MURDER
PERJURY
PIRACY
POACHING
ROBBERY

SABOTAGE
SHOPLIFTING
STALKING
TERRORISM
THEFT
TREASON
VANDALISM

SWEETS

BONBON
CARAMEL
CHEWING GUM
FONDANT
FRUIT JELLY
FUDGE
GUMDROP

HALVA
JELLY BEAN
LEMON DROP
LOLLIPOP
LOZENGE
MARSHMALLOW
MARZIPAN

NOISETTE
NOUGAT
PEPPERMINT
PRALINE
TOFFEE
TRUFFLE
TURKISH DELIGHT

F	L	E	H	S	E	C	I	N	E	S	R	A	L	E
D	E	C	E	P	T	I	O	N	I	S	L	A	N	D
L	A	F	R	B	W	A	X	D	C	O	K	S	T	D
M	U	I	Y	A	A	T	E	R	N	R	N	E	A	N
O	L	S	O	Y	R	P	I	S	I	N	E	U	E	A
U	A	S	R	O	T	E	P	L	S	H	K	L	L	L
N	K	A	K	F	Y	N	L	E	S	S	A	T	T	S
T	E	M	C	W	S	G	H	E	T	H	O	R	T	T
S	V	N	O	H	Q	U	C	E	W	R	S	R	O	A
I	O	O	L	A	U	I	T	R	E	S	E	D	C	O
D	S	S	T	L	I	N	E	G	A	H	S	L	S	C
L	T	N	R	E	D	L	S	G	R	E	B	E	C	I
E	O	I	O	S	L	R	I	V	E	R	O	N	Y	X
Y	K	V	P	I	F	R	E	S	H	W	A	T	E	R
O	I	S	K	S	U	B	E	R	E	T	N	U	O	M

ALL ABOUT ANTARCTICA

BAY OF WHALES
COATS LAND
DECEPTION ISLAND
DESERT
FRESH WATER
ICEBERGS
ICE SHEET
KILLER WHALE

KRILL
LAKE VOSTOK
LARSEN ICE SHELF
MOUNT EREBUS
MOUNT SIDLEY
PENGUIN
PETREL
PORT LOCKROY

RIVER ONYX
ROSS SEA
SCOTT
SHAG
SKUA
TERN
VINSON MASSIF
WARTY SQUID

TYPES OF SNAKE

BOA
BROWN SNAKE
CARPET SNAKE
COBRA
CONSTRICTOR
COPPERHEAD
DIPSAS
DUGITE
GARTER SNAKE

GRASS SNAKE
INDIGO SNAKE
KRAIT
LANGAHA
MAMBA
PINE SNAKE
RACER
RAT SNAKE
RINGHALS

SAND SNAKE
SEA SNAKE
SIDEWINDER
TAIPAN
TREE SNAKE
WATER SNAKE
WORM SNAKE

E	I	D	O	G	A	L	T	B	I	E	R	I	E	D
X	T	R	A	C	R	E	A	M	A	L	E	Z	C	U
P	H	A	B	N	R	E	E	B	T	I	U	R	F	A
O	A	U	B	R	N	R	E	R	E	E	B	G	E	K
R	S	G	E	R	E	E	V	N	U	A	A	A	R	I
T	W	H	Y	D	O	B	I	G	B	L	R	M	E	S
L	E	T	B	U	A	W	R	V	T	E	W	B	E	E
A	I	M	E	N	D	E	N	R	G	I	E	E	B	L
M	Z	I	E	K	N	I	A	A	N	E	K	R	Y	L
B	E	L	R	E	E	P	L	T	L	E	E	A	E	E
I	N	D	S	L	P	K	E	A	I	E	L	L	N	H
C	B	L	A	I	C	R	L	R	E	I	H	E	O	I
E	I	D	S	A	A	A	K	T	Y	D	N	A	H	S
P	E	T	L	L	E	R	E	E	B	E	C	I	R	E
R	R	B	E	R	O	B	I	T	T	E	R	E	N	M

TYPES OF BEER

ABBEY BEER
ALTBIER
AMBER ALE
BITTER
BLACK LAGER
BROWN ALE
CREAM ALE
DRAUGHT
DUNKEL
EXPORT

FRUIT BEER
GREEN BEER
GUEUZE
HELLES
HONEY BEER
KEG BEER
KRIEK
LAMBIC
MILD
PILSENER

REAL ALE
RED ALE
RICE BEER
SAHTI
SHANDY
TRAPPIST
VIENNA
WEIZENBIER
WINTER ALE

R	L	T	I	R	X	I	A	E	B	T	N	U	R	G
M	L	A	E	V	E	R	N	E	C	R	E	L	Y	S
U	V	E	E	Y	R	T	T	R	I	E	G	A	K	
T	C	P	T	E	L	R	O	N	I	A	O	Y	O	R
T	O	E	A	A	A	P	Y	R	K	M	R	V	E	A
E	N	R	R	Y	I	A	M	T	T	E	A	R	I	M
R	F	I	O	F	W	C	C	I	T	R	A	T	H	E
L	E	P	T	A	Y	U	N	A	L	L	G	W	E	R
L	S	R	E	D	R	O	T	U	C	I	E	U	S	R
E	S	V	K	T	Q	S	M	E	N	T	I	O	N	E
T	I	A	S	U	N	I	D	T	N	E	M	M	O	C
G	I	N	I	E	Z	I	C	I	L	B	U	P	Y	I
Z	I	P	M	C	I	L	B	U	P	E	K	A	M	T
E	D	A	E	R	A	R	T	I	C	U	L	A	T	E
C	I	L	T	P	D	I	S	C	L	O	S	E	L	S

JUST SAYING

ARTICULATE
BETRAY
COMMENT
CONFESS
DECLARE
DISCLOSE
ENUNCIATE
GIVE AWAY
GRUNT
IMPLY

INSTRUCT
INTIMATE
LEAK
MAKE PUBLIC
MENTION
MUTTER
ORATE
ORDER
PUBLICIZE
QUIP

READ
RECITE
REMARK
REPEAT
RETORT
REVEAL
SAY
STATE
TELL
VOICE

P	S	R	L	I	B	R	E	G	R	A	T	S	A	E
N	C	E	T	I	H	P	G	C	T	K	R	Q	S	R
K	N	U	M	P	I	H	C	S	I	M	U	U	R	N
R	R	B	I	P	F	F	L	B	B	E	P	I	K	A
A	F	V	A	E	E	G	L	T	B	L	T	R	A	J
A	O	C	Q	R	O	R	E	R	A	E	V	R	O	A
I	A	A	R	P	E	S	C	Q	R	O	E	E	P	U
I	U	E	H	T	U	V	P	A	L	T	M	L	P	V
R	T	E	S	O	A	L	P	E	P	P	R	Y	H	T
R	R	M	M	I	A	O	O	I	O	Y	O	I	Y	E
E	A	R	B	R	B	R	B	N	B	C	B	P	R	O
H	O	H	C	R	Y	O	O	R	Y	I	E	A	O	P
D	M	B	R	E	V	A	E	B	E	J	B	B	R	R
G	I	P	A	E	N	I	U	G	L	J	U	M	E	A
Y	K	E	E	R	A	H	C	E	L	A	R	S	A	E

TYPES OF RODENT

BEAVER	GERBIL	PIKA
CAPYBARA	GOPHER	RABBIT
CHIPMUNK	GUINEA PIG	RAT
COYPU	HAMSTER	SQUIRREL
DORMOUSE	HARE	VOLE
FERRET	JERBOA	

SPANISH NUMBERS

CATORCE
CERO
CIEN
CINCO
CINCUENTA
CUARENTA
CUATRO
DIEZ
DOCE

DOS
NOVENTA
NUEVE
OCHENTA
OCHO
ONCE
QUINCE
SEIS
SESENTA

SETENTA
SIETE
TRECE
TREINTA
TRES
UNO
VEINTE

R	E	G	G	O	R	F	S	T	S	U	O	J	P	B
I	O	E	T	N	A	C	A	P	N	O	E	N	O	N
T	O	W	C	R	R	B	E	R	Z	E	R	K	L	A
R	R	S	F	A	S	T	E	R	O	I	D	S	E	I
G	I	A	M	O	O	N	P	A	T	R	O	L	P	N
A	A	B	C	T	D	E	F	E	N	D	E	R	O	O
E	L	O	E	K	B	R	Z	A	X	X	O	N	S	C
E	S	M	L	D	A	Y	A	T	N	A	G	O	I	S
A	N	S	G	I	S	N	O	Z	S	I	N	O	T	O
G	O	P	Y	G	Q	U	D	B	I	E	E	G	I	B
A	G	A	R	D	B	Q	O	F	R	W	P	M	O	N
L	A	C	U	U	E	U	I	I	I	E	A	M	N	P
A	R	M	S	G	R	E	R	X	V	E	P	R	E	A
G	D	A	S	A	T	G	N	O	P	E	L	A	K	T
C	E	N	T	I	P	E	D	E	T	O	X	D	P	U

CLASSIC ARCADE GAMES

ASTEROIDS	GYRUSS	QIX
BERZERK	JOUST	SCRAMBLE
BOSCONIAN	MOON PATROL	TEMPEST
CENTIPEDE	MS PAC-MAN	TRACK AND FIELD
DEFENDER	PAPERBOY	WIZARD OF WOR
DIG DUG	PENGO	XEVIOUS
DRAGON'S LAIR	POLE POSITION	ZAXXON
FROGGER	PONG	
GALAGA	QBERT	

SEATS

BANQUETTE	DIVAN	PEW
BEANBAG	LOUNGER	SADDLE
BENCH	LOVE SEAT	SETTEE
CHAISE LONGUE	OTTOMAN	SOFA
COUCH	PALANQUIN	STOOL
DECKCHAIR	PERCH	THRONE

PENINSULAS

ALASKA
ARABIAN
ARDS
AVALON
BALKAN
BATAAN
BOOTHIA
CAPE COD
CHUKCHI
CRIMEA

DECCAN
EYRE
FLORIDA
GASPE
GOWER
IBERIA
ISTRIA
JUTLAND
KINTYRE
KOLA

KOWLOON
LEIZHOU
LLYN
MALAY
PALMER
SINAI
TASMAN
WIRRAL
YORKE

C	N	S	M	S	T	O	O	B	Y	K	N	I	K	S
R	E	O	I	E	B	I	G	R	I	V	E	R	L	P
K	S	C	T	H	S	N	L	E	S	O	T	T	E	R
S	N	C	O	L	P	S	E	N	T	A	H	K	S	I
T	A	R	J	N	I	M	O	T	O	V	E	T	M	N
H	H	A	E	B	T	M	E	F	I	E	B	H	I	G
G	N	Z	R	R	P	A	A	M	L	N	A	E	S	A
I	A	Y	S	S	A	Y	C	H	L	U	N	L	E	W
E	V	F	E	T	S	O	S	T	E	E	D	I	R	A
H	E	O	Y	A	S	C	V	M	Y	Q	S	O	A	K
E	R	R	B	C	I	S	O	E	L	Y	V	N	B	E
H	A	Y	O	N	O	H	E	C	L	A	I	K	L	N
T	E	O	Y	N	N	N	N	N	I	N	S	I	E	I
N	D	U	S	U	T	S	B	O	B	S	I	N	S	N
I	R	C	F	C	I	N	A	T	I	T	T	G	T	G

TONY-WINNING MUSICALS

AVENUE Q
BIG RIVER
BILLY ELLIOT
CATS
CONTACT
CRAZY FOR YOU
DEAR EVAN HANSEN
FOSSE

FUN HOME
HAMILTON
IN THE HEIGHTS
JERSEY BOYS
KINKY BOOTS
LES MISERABLES
MEMPHIS
ONCE

PASSION
RENT
SPRING AWAKENING
THE BAND'S VISIT
THE LION KING
TITANIC

T	T	A	B	N	E	G	A	T	E	S	O	L	T	O
C	B	A	E	A	B	R	A	S	I	O	N	O	R	E
E	L	A	B	S	U	R	D	H	O	E	B	E	E	E
J	T	A	N	R	A	R	A	S	R	B	L	D	A	T
B	N	A	N	A	U	B	E	U	A	B	A	E	B	N
A	A	B	A	I	U	P	J	L	A	R	A	A	E	E
B	Y	O	B	T	G	B	T	B	B	B	B	A	R	S
D	E	V	A	R	A	I	N	A	U	S	Y	S	R	B
O	B	E	G	A	A	G	R	N	C	A	T	H	A	A
M	A	A	B	O	U	N	D	O	B	A	S	R	N	M
E	I	E	T	A	B	A	N	R	B	I	A	O	T	O
N	U	B	B	U	N	D	O	E	L	A	E	A	S	B
O	V	S	B	T	R	A	D	O	A	T	R	O	B	A
Y	E	B	B	A	D	B	B	A	C	A	B	O	D	E
A	B	S	E	I	L	A	E	N	O	L	A	B	A	A

WORDS STARTING AB

ABALONE
ABATE
ABBEY
ABBOT
ABDOMEN
ABED
ABERRANT
ABEYANT
ABJECT
ABJURE

ABLER
ABLUSH
ABNEGATE
ABODE
ABOLISH
ABORIGINAL
ABORT
ABOUND
ABOVE
ABRADE

ABRASION
ABREAST
ABROAD
ABRUPT
ABSCOND
ABSEIL
ABSENTEE
ABSURD
ABUNDANT
ABUT

P	A	R	S	L	E	Y	R	A	M	E	S	O	R	I
R	E	I	B	C	D	F	L	J	U	N	I	P	E	R
B	O	D	L	I	I	L	D	E	E	V	O	L	C	A
J	L	S	L	F	S	R	P	E	D	B	E	T	E	L
H	A	L	A	P	E	A	E	R	E	P	P	E	P	N
Y	P	S	I	F	P	N	A	M	A	S	W	O	I	R
S	M	C	M	R	F	T	N	C	R	C	I	M	E	D
S	E	I	I	I	S	R	H	E	C	U	U	N	A	O
O	L	K	N	U	N	I	O	A	L	C	T	L	A	O
P	A	R	M	T	V	E	M	N	E	G	H	I	W	W
N	U	T	M	E	G	U	C	D	E	A	Y	S	A	M
S	H	W	S	F	S	E	A	I	A	R	M	A	S	R
S	E	L	F	A	E	L	Y	A	B	L	E	B	A	O
T	F	H	O	R	S	E	R	A	D	I	S	H	B	W
E	M	I	L	R	I	F	F	A	K	C	R	M	I	C

HERBS AND SPICES

ALLSPICE
ALOE
ANISEED
BASIL
BAY LEAF
BETEL
CHIVES
CLOVE
CUMIN
DILL

FENNEL
GARLIC
HORSERADISH
HYSSOP
JASMINE
JUNIPER
KAFFIR LIME
MINT
MUSTARD
NUTMEG

PAPRIKA
PARSLEY
PEPPER
ROSEMARY
SAFFRON
SUMAC
THYME
TURMERIC
WASABI
WORMWOOD

D	N	G	K	D	E	L	N	A	R	B	E	Z	G	R
E	O	R	D	G	O	B	L	I	N	O	P	S	N	E
L	M	E	R	A	A	G	E	I	E	U	L	B	I	P
L	E	E	E	E	E	R	F	L	G	E	E	F	K	L
I	L	N	B	S	H	H	E	I	E	N	H	P	S	U
R	G	L	A	I	R	S	L	P	S	O	E	L	A	G
F	A	A	M	L	L	U	E	L	P	H	P	V	B	H
R	E	N	B	K	O	R	N	R	U	O	E	A	E	H
E	B	D	O	Y	S	A	N	D	H	B	C	R	R	S
G	R	C	O	O	K	I	E	C	U	T	T	E	R	D
I	O	D	A	E	H	R	E	M	M	A	H	E	E	O
T	P	U	P	I	T	K	C	A	L	B	O	F	B	K
P	I	T	R	E	V	L	I	S	R	O	U	G	H	A
N	A	E	G	R	E	A	T	W	H	I	T	E	E	M
H	L	E	I	P	O	R	T	J	A	C	K	S	O	N

SHARKS

BAMBOO	GREAT WHITE	REEF
BASKING	GREENLAND	ROUGH
BLACKTIP	GULPER	SAND
BLUE	HAMMERHEAD	SEVENGILL
BULLHEAD	LEMON	SILKY
COOKIECUTTER	LEOPARD	SILVERTIP
COPPER	MAKO	SLEEPER
DOGFISH	NURSE	THRESHER
FRILLED	PORBEAGLE	TIGER
GOBLIN	PORT JACKSON	ZEBRA

Y	I	G	O	D	R	O	B	L	U	S	H	O	D	V
M	R	G	N	S	E	U	N	E	U	Y	S	S	E	V
A	E	R	M	I	D	I	B	I	O	L	R	O	R	I
M	T	D	E	S	L	R	F	Y	F	E	I	R	E	N
O	D	U	I	H	B	K	Y	I	P	S	D	O	S	T
N	E	T	R	U	S	T	R	S	T	O	E	L	U	A
T	T	D	R	B	M	T	R	A	H	R	R	O	O	G
I	I	E	I	O	E	S	E	O	P	E	O	T	H	E
L	H	L	T	W	P	C	H	E	P	S	R	F	U	P
L	W	L	E	A	P	E	I	E	W	Y	E	R	D	O
A	E	U	T	R	B	S	T	N	R	S	N	E	Y	R
D	S	M	R	T	L	L	W	I	O	R	T	W	T	T
O	U	V	R	S	R	R	E	W	H	T	Y	T	A	I
Y	O	K	C	E	S	I	M	E	D	W	L	T	E	T
G	H	E	E	R	F	L	O	H	O	C	L	A	R	H

TYPES OF WINE

ALCOHOL-FREE
AMONTILLADO
BLUSH
BRUT
DEMI-SEC
DRY SHERRY
FINO
FORTIFIED

HOUSE RED
HOUSE WHITE
MEDIUM SHERRY
MULLED
OLOROSO
ROSE
RUBY PORT
SPARKLING

STRAW
SWEET SHERRY
TABLE
TAWNY PORT
TONIC
VINTAGE PORT
WHITE PORT

T	U	O	E	K	I	R	T	S	B	C	R	E	D	P
C	D	G	K	R	N	H	D	O	N	P	I	U	L	A
H	F	R	S	O	D	I	K	O	C	E	G	G	A	C
E	I	C	A	S	E	T	G	O	O	H	A	D	L
S	R	A	M	O	T	R	A	L	U	E	T	E	O	L
T	S	T	E	H	B	C	I	T	O	B	F	L	B	A
P	T	C	C	E	H	E	E	P	R	V	I	R	A	B
R	B	H	A	L	R	U	R	R	M	S	E	O	T	E
O	A	E	F	M	G	E	M	O	R	U	L	N	T	S
T	S	R	F	E	N	C	E	I	C	T	D	I	E	A
E	E	P	O	T	S	T	R	O	H	S	E	M	R	B
C	M	F	O	U	L	L	I	N	E	I	R	R	S	O
T	A	G	R	I	S	E	T	A	L	P	E	M	O	H
O	N	A	M	E	S	A	B	D	N	O	C	E	S	U
R	U	N	N	E	R	O	S	G	N	I	N	N	I	F

BASEBALL GAME

BASEBALL CAP	FIRST BASEMAN	RIGHT FIELDER
BATTER	FOUL LINE	RUNNER
CATCHER	GLOVE	SCOREBOARD
CHEST PROTECTOR	HELMET	SECOND BASEMAN
COACH	HIT	SHORTSTOP
DUGOUT	HOME PLATE	STRIKEOUT
FACE MASK	INNINGS	UMPIRE
FENCE	MINOR LEAGUE	

KINGS AND QUEENS

AETHELBALD
AETHELBERT
ALFRED
CANUTE
CAROLINE
EADRED
EDGAR
EDMUND
EDRED
EDWARD

ELEANOR
FRANCIS
GEORGE
HELEN
HENRY
ISABEL
JOHN
LOTHAIR
LOUIS
MARIE ANTOINETTE

MATILDA
PENELOPE
PEPIN
PERSEPHONE
PHILIP
RUDOLPH
SHEBA
STEPHEN
TITANIA
ZENOBIA

M	T	L	T	E	E	E	L	Y	R	A	P	I	D	S
A	C	R	A	R	E	E	F	L	R	M	I	T	T	D
R	R	G	H	I	L	A	N	A	C	A	A	A	N	A
S	E	T	N	B	R	O	A	D	S	D	U	O	E	A
H	E	R	N	O	S	T	R	A	I	T	P	T	R	R
L	K	E	E	B	M	C	E	L	O	C	H	S	A	
L	R	I	Y	N	E	A	S	W	A	M	P	I	B	E
A	T	N	R	A	T	S	L	E	K	A	L	H	Y	U
F	E	A	T	L	E	D	O	L	D	T	A	A	T	A
R	L	K	N	O	T	K	I	U	I	M	A	I	E	T
E	U	O	A	R	R	D	L	D	N	B	N	S	S	E
T	V	O	E	B	A	Y	O	U	T	D	L	O	T	L
A	I	R	C	R	C	S	A	M	A	E	R	T	S	N
W	R	B	O	R	E	S	P	R	I	N	G	O	A	I
R	I	V	E	R	T	R	I	B	U	T	A	R	Y	F

WATER FEATURES

BAYOU
BILLABONG
BROADS
BROOK
CANAL
CREEK
DELTA
ESTUARY
INLET

LAKE
LOCH
MARSH
OCEAN
POND
RAPIDS
REEF
RIVER
RIVULET

SEA
SOUND
SPRING
STRAIT
STREAM
SWAMP
TARN
TRIBUTARY
WATERFALL

O	X	S	T	C	O	R	E	D	U	M	P	E	W	L
S	P	L	U	G	I	N	L	T	S	T	T	M	C	P
T	P	I	R	C	S	S	W	O	D	N	I	W	H	R
R	A	R	F	A	R	E	D	L	O	F	L	S	A	S
E	C	C	E	P	C	S	P	A	S	S	W	O	R	D
K	K	B	C	A	M	O	I	C	O	N	M	E	A	F
C	A	F	L	E	D	E	L	W	L	K	E	H	C	I
E	G	F	O	F	S	S	T	D	C	R	N	C	T	R
H	E	O	G	T	S	S	H	A	B	M	U	A	E	E
C	D	G	O	P	U	D	R	E	F	O	D	C	R	W
S	L	O	N	N	B	C	T	O	E	I	O	L	C	A
U	O	L	I	I	I	I	C	S	A	T	L	T	O	L
R	G	X	O	O	A	U	T	O	S	A	V	E	D	L
I	I	S	S	W	S	C	R	O	L	L	C	E	E
V	N	U	S	E	R	I	N	T	E	R	F	A	C	E

COMPUTING TERMS

ACCESS	FOLDER	PASSWORD
ASCII	FTP	PLUG IN
AUTOSAVE	ICON	SCRIPT
BIOS	LOGIN	SCROLL
CACHE	LOG OFF	SPREADSHEET
CHARACTER CODE	LOG ON	UNIX
COLD BOOT	MENU	URL
CORE DUMP	METAFILE	USER INTERFACE
CRACK	MS-DOS	VIRUS CHECKER
FIREWALL	PACKAGE	WINDOWS

```
P M U J O F U R L O N G E A E
S T E W A R D S E N Q U I R Y
M R I F P A C I D N A H G J N
L K T F O S E I K O O B U U I
G N I O G A I E R A M I T V D
N T S T E E P L E C H A S E E
I A A F T C P C V W S Y T N H
C E A O O A K L A E Y D M I G
A Y G R T R O C A T R V D L I
R A E M I N D A O C C R A E E
T W L A R E D N E D E I I E W
A H D L S D S L N D D C T N H
L C I B L I N K E R S A S C G
F A N A S A G O O D E E P A G
A E G V H M A I U E C I V O N
```

HORSE RACING TERMS

BLINKERS	GOOD	PADDOCK
BOOKIE	HANDICAP	PLACE
EACH WAY	HEAVY	SILVER RING
FIRM	JUMP	SOFT
FLAT RACING	JUVENILE	STEEPLECHASE
FORM	MAIDEN RACE	STEWARD'S ENQUIRY
FURLONG	MARE	TIC-TAC
GELDING	NOVICE	TOTE
GOING	ODDS	WEIGHED IN

```
O F T N N T O I W L F V U J Q
I R O W B N H G O I O B N U A
F D I X T C C E R V E V I S E
F E A E H V N T L E T T V T E
A V V Y I Q W T D W I K I I R
L T T U S B U V V E O R S C E
V A I I T T F B T L N O I E P
S N Z V V S A V O L L W O N A
E N O T S T N R R N I T N E C
I E C E C B S R T E F E L T S
V T N M T E H S E T E N O W E
O N O E V H C B R W L Y E O G
M A I R R B E P U O T M S R T
E L E T A E R C O R Y Z I K R
B O U N C E T V W K V T T R O
```

TV NETWORKS

ABC	GETTV	NBC
ANTENNA TV	GRIT	PBS
BOUNCE TV	HSN	QUBO
CBS	ION LIFE	QVC
CNN	JUSTICE NETWORK	RETRO TV
COZI TV	LAFF	THE CW
CREATE	LIVE WELL NETWORK	THIS TV
DAYSTAR	METV	UNIVISION
ESCAPE	MOVIES	WORLD
FOX	MYNETWORKTV	

```
N  A  I  T  P  Y  G  E  A  H  J  G  N  D  E
B  Y  Z  A  N  T  I  N  E  F  R  H  T  E  N
A  B  A  A  C  O  C  L  L  E  O  S  S  A  C
N  N  M  E  U  H  L  O  G  A  N  I  I  H  S
O  O  T  G  I  E  R  O  S  J  S  R  H  I  A
R  Z  N  N  E  R  M  A  W  T  I  D  N  A  A
A  I  E  I  N  I  N  V  E  S  T  R  D  D  R
M  S  C  T  A  C  A  D  A  D  N  U  U  U  A
E  E  I  N  I  N  I  O  N  A  N  N  B  E  L
A  N  N  T  E  S  R  E  K  N  O  I  H  N  O
E  U  T  S  H  O  Y  A  A  A  L  C  B  E  S
I  A  E  N  Z  E  S  C  O  P  T  I  C  P  I
H  E  B  R  E  W  S  J  U  L  I  A  N  A  A
L  N  G  E  R  M  A  N  I  C  I  V  I  L  H
B  A  B  Y  L  O  N  I  A  N  T  A  Y  I  T
```

CALENDARS

AKAN
ASSYRIAN
ATTIC
AZTEC
BABYLONIAN
BUDDHIST
BYZANTINE
CHINESE
COPTIC

EGYPTIAN
FLORENTINE
GERMANIC
GREGORIAN
HEBREW
HELLENIC
HINDU
IRISH
JAVANESE

JULIAN
MINGUO
NEPALI
ROMAN
RUNIC
SWEDISH
THAI SOLAR
ZOROASTRIAN

```
Y L E N A E B I L L I H C N K
A R D Y E N A E B O T N I P C
A P A S P A R A G U S B E A N
A I E N N A E B B O R A C C A
T N N A B M U N G B E A N E
N U A N A E B I K U Z D A N B
F A O E A E B N E A L E D A Y
N L E R B E B T A N G Y B E E
A B A B P D B H O E C E T B N
E U A G K S E R C C B A E Y D
B R N L E C N G E N I X A O I
A D E R B O A A N N E R A S K
M N E A U A L L E I N R A W D
I B O A E O L E B B W U F H E
L N A E B R E T T U B E R E R
```

TYPES OF BEAN

ADZUKI BEAN
ASPARAGUS BEAN
BEAN SPROUT
BLACK BEAN
BUTTER BEAN
CAROB BEAN
CHILLI BEAN

FLAGEOLET
FRENCH BEAN
HARICOT BEAN
LABLAB
LIMA BEAN
MUNG BEAN
PINTO BEAN

RED KIDNEY BEAN
RUNNER BEAN
SOYBEAN
URD
WAX BEAN
WINGED BEAN

R	E	T	U	R	M	H	E	N	I	T	R	A	M	C
L	E	E	M	A	I	A	S	W	K	I	M	M	E	L
C	C	M	L	S	L	M	A	A	I	K	V	L	S	C
N	O	A	U	N	K	R	S	O	N	S	C	R	R	L
A	U	L	E	H	S	O	M	T	B	D	A	O	I	L
M	R	B	B	R	C	M	O	U	E	R	L	H	R	M
R	C	A	R	E	A	S	A	R	R	W	I	E	I	S
E	A	B	S	R	R	L	E	I	B	P	A	E	R	G
V	R	K	H	M	S	T	L	I	L	E	H	R	N	E
L	R	R	B	R	A	N	D	E	N	L	L	Y	T	R
I	E	M	N	O	L	L	A	F	N	F	I	L	M	V
S	Y	L	N	I	L	T	L	E	R	E	E	W	S	A
L	E	R	U	A	L	E	H	Y	U	R	E	L	M	I
N	D	N	T	E	N	O	H	N	N	I	N	O	D	S
I	W	U	R	D	C	F	C	I	O	Y	D	R	A	H

COMEDIANS

ALLEN
BRAND
BROOKS
CARREY
COHEN
COLBERT
FALLON

GERVAIS
HARDY
KIMMEL
LAUREL
MARTIN
MURPHY
O'BRIEN

ROCK
SANDLER
SCHUMER
SEINFELD
SILVERMAN
STEWART
WILLIAMS

```
T  I  R  E  D  D  S  T  D  E  N  I  A  R  D
O  O  I  S  S  E  S  O  B  E  D  T  I  M  E
P  X  T  E  C  Y  E  G  N  I  Z  O  D  R  N
A  W  R  H  I  E  R  T  R  E  S  T  I  N  G
N  N  A  E  G  Y  T  S  L  U  G  G  I  S  H
T  A  N  Y  R  V  T  V  N  S  N  G  L  O  G
A  P  C  E  A  A  A  E  A  I  T  D  Y  G  D
C  P  E  T  H  E  M  Z  R  U  R  R  N  E  Y
S  I  S  U  T  H  Z  E  O  E  A  I  U  A  S
O  N  O  H  E  Z  B  N  A  E  Z  G  T  W  W
T  G  P  S  L  M  R  M  W  O  I  S  G  O  O
F  S  E  B  U  O  I  R  O  T  E  Y  U  L  R
D  L  R  L  W  N  E  N  A  I  A  U  T  L  D
E  O  S  N  G  V  S  F  S  K  N  U  B  I  T
E  W  D  R  O  P  O  F  F  T  H  A  S  P  H
```

FEELING SLEEPY

BEDTIME
BUNK
CATNAP
DOZING
DRAINED
DREAMING
DROP OFF
DROWSY
FATIGUED

HEAVY-EYED
LETHARGIC
MATTRESS
NAPPING
OVERWEARY
PILLOW
REPOSE
RESTING
SHUT-EYE

SIESTA
SLOW
SLUGGISH
SLUMBERING
SNOOZING
TIRED
TRANCE
WORN OUT
ZZZ

U	R	A	N	O	Y	R	A	K	I	R	E	P	L	T
T	A	E	I	I	U	P	F	N	O	T	Y	C	L	S
T	E	A	X	C	D	A	E	E	I	E	R	E	E	U
Y	L	S	G	C	C	U	P	I	G	B	C	L	Y	X
R	H	S	P	I	I	I	S	A	S	O	C	E	O	E
O	C	G	A	A	C	T	N	A	C	U	I	C	P	L
S	O	L	H	R	N	G	O	R	I	T	T	H	P	
S	R	Y	I	I	L	Y	A	R	A	O	S	R	T	R
E	T	T	P	I	R	N	S	C	T	N	U	O	H	A
C	I	O	O	A	I	O	P	T	I	C	O	T	A	L
C	R	N	N	A	N	O	X	A	C	R	C	O	L	O
A	B	L	L	A	U	G	N	I	L	P	A	N	M	S
L	U	G	E	N	I	C	U	L	A	T	E	U	I	N
V	A	G	U	S	A	B	D	U	C	E	N	S	C	R
R	A	D	I	A	L	P	M	Y	E	L	O	N	R	Y

NERVES

ABDUCENS
ACCESSORY
ACOUSTIC
AXON
BOUTON
CRANIAL
CYTON
ELECTROTONUS
EPICRITIC

EXCITOR
FACIAL
GANGLION
GENICULATE
LINGUAL
MYELON
NIDUS
OPHTHALMIC
OPTIC

PERIKARYON
RADIAL
SCIATIC
SOLAR PLEXUS
SYNAPSE
TROCHLEAR
ULNAR
VAGUS

F	P	P	N	N	T	E	T	O	F	C	D	L	P	C
O	S	A	F	R	H	C	T	E	O	T	L	N	C	E
R	E	M	S	I	E	O	E	R	N	I	T	O	I	L
M	A	T	N	L	T	E	N	E	R	N	P	S	F	
A	R	E	N	O	E	E	N	V	N	P	E	P	A	E
T	C	I	H	P	A	R	G	I	A	O	L	T	U	C
N	H	N	E	T	W	O	R	K	O	S	C	A	N	T
P	R	I	N	T	E	R	P	E	N	P	S	S	C	I
A	A	N	N	E	S	A	B	A	T	A	D	E	I	E
C	O	M	M	A	N	D	H	N	E	P	O	L	N	D
N	N	T	R	E	C	E	I	V	E	E	R	C	O	D
E	T	E	L	E	D	I	E	W	T	C	E	L	E	S
Y	P	O	C	T	D	C	C	F	I	C	L	I	C	K
O	F	O	N	T	E	R	A	W	T	F	O	S	T	T
M	A	A	R	U	N	E	M	A	N	O	C	I	I	P

USING THE COMPUTER

CLICK
CLOSE
COMMAND
COPY
CUT
DATABASE
DELETE
DISCONNECT
FILE
FIND

FONT
FORMAT
GRAPHIC
ICON
INPUT
INTERNET
MENU
NETWORK
OPEN
PASTE

POINTER
PRINTER
RECEIVE
REPLACE
SAVE
SEARCH
SELECT
SEND
SOFTWARE

S	F	R	A	M	E	S	S	T	I	N	G	I	N	G
Y	D	O	O	R	B	S	M	O	K	E	R	I	A	B
I	N	S	T	A	R	L	A	R	V	A	E	E	W	E
M	R	A	W	S	L	L	E	C	N	E	C	T	A	R
B	E	E	S	W	A	X	S	E	V	O	L	G	E	E
D	B	E	E	S	U	I	T	E	E	E	G	N	R	K
W	A	G	G	L	E	D	A	N	C	E	O	N	E	R
S	G	N	I	T	F	A	R	G	O	R	E	G	S	O
R	I	Y	N	O	L	O	C	N	D	S	E	V	N	W
N	O	C	O	M	B	C	E	D	T	I	B	L	I	L
G	E	T	H	G	I	L	F	G	N	I	T	A	M	H
W	E	E	D	Y	L	L	E	J	L	A	Y	O	R	O
O	L	O	U	O	S	G	G	E	G	L	E	Y	L	E
V	O	T	P	Q	F	P	H	E	R	O	M	O	N	E
G	N	I	T	S	E	V	R	A	H	O	N	E	Y	R

BEEKEEPING

BEE SUIT
BEESWAX
BROOD
CELLS
COLONY
COMB
DRONE
EGGS
FRAMES

GLOVES
GRAFTING
HARVESTING
HIVE
HONEY
INSTAR LARVAE
MATING FLIGHT
NECTAR
NEST

PHEROMONE
POLLEN
QUEEN
ROYAL JELLY
SMOKER
STINGING
SWARM
WAGGLE DANCE
WORKER

AGRICULTURAL EQUIPMENT

BALER	HEDGE TRIMMER	SCYTHE
CHAINSAW	IRRIGATOR	SEED DRILL
CORN DRILL	PITCHFORK	SHOVEL
FORKLIFT TRUCK	POTATO PLANTER	SICKLE
HARROW	POWER LIFT	SPADE
HARVESTER	REAPING HOOK	TANKER
HAYFORK	ROTARY HOE	TRACTOR
HAYRAKE	SCARIFIER	TRAILER

Y	U	A	M	B	I	G	U	O	U	S	A	D	A	E
D	N	M	Y	K	R	U	M	R	P	N	E	D	A	D
U	C	H	E	E	R	L	E	S	S	A	V	A	E	U
O	L	I	L	P	S	A	S	M	M	W	L	P	N	N
L	E	L	B	G	A	M	I	S	T	Y	R	U	I	I
C	A	E	A	B	S	L	N	E	U	E	A	D	A	N
I	R	A	T	E	L	A	P	E	S	D	O	Y	T	T
N	R	D	A	Y	D	Y	Y	S	H	U	G	R	R	E
D	D	E	B	Y	D	I	I	M	B	S	I	A	E	R
I	I	N	E	A	G	N	S	T	O	S	A	E	C	E
L	E	L	D	E	G	G	F	M	K	O	E	R	N	S
H	A	U	L	P	D	U	O	T	A	R	L	D	U	T
U	N	I	N	A	L	I	R	F	R	L	A	G	W	I
B	L	E	A	K	P	N	M	K	C	N	S	D	K	N
L	D	U	L	L	O	V	E	R	C	A	S	T	A	G

EVERYTHING'S BLEAK

AMBIGUOUS
ASHEN
BLEAK
CHEERLESS
CLOUDY
DARK
DEBATABLE
DEPRESSING
DIM

DISMAL
DOUBTFUL
DREARY
DULL
FOGGY
GLOOMY
LEADEN
MISTY
MURKY

OVERCAST
PALE
PALLID
UNCERTAIN
UNCLEAR
UNINTERESTING
WAN

E	D	L	E	I	F	S	N	A	M	S	N	U	N	S
S	N	S	N	E	E	U	Q	E	H	T	O	E	O	T
O	N	T	O	S	L	T	M	N	E	H	T	I	S	C
N	U	H	H	M	D	B	O	N	A	I	E	T	F	R
E	F	U	E	X	E	T	E	R	S	L	L	S	L	O
S	F	G	E	K	R	R	T	K	S	D	P	I	O	S
A	I	H	E	E	O	F	V	N	N	A	M	R	W	S
R	E	S	M	R	O	R	H	I	K	S	E	H	L	M
B	L	E	T	R	C	O	B	E	L	T	T	C	B	Y
E	D	N	D	P	J	A	L	M	S	L	N	S	A	T
W	E	N	E	T	E	L	N	E	E	O	E	U	L	I
I	H	A	S	N	O	T	C	I	R	P	E	P	I	N
W	I	T	N	G	L	R	E	I	L	T	R	R	O	I
R	Q	S	G	A	O	G	E	R	O	C	G	O	L	R
S	E	U	O	W	H	L	J	E	S	U	S	C	H	T

OXFORD COLLEGES

BALIOL	LINACRE	ST CROSS
BRASENOSE	MANSFIELD	ST HILDA'S
CORPUS CHRISTI	MERTON	ST HUGH'S
EXETER	NEW	ST JOHN'S
GREEN TEMPLETON	NUFFIELD	ST PETER'S
HARTFORD	ORIEL	THE QUEEN'S
JESUS	PEMBROKE	TRINITY
KEBLE	SOMERVILLE	WOLFSON
KELLOGG	ST ANNE'S	WORCESTER

T	A	M	I	L	B	P	A	N	I	I	A	O	U	I
E	G	N	O	R	I	Y	A	A	N	N	W	H	D	D
S	A	N	N	R	I	R	B	R	A	B	A	Y	A	D
E	A	J	R	P	H	T	A	G	H	I	D	D	N	T
M	D	N	A	D	U	R	A	O	T	L	H	E	I	I
I	H	D	N	I	S	I	J	T	S	A	I	R	T	T
K	R	A	A	L	N	P	N	A	A	G	I	A	T	A
K	I	A	N	R	U	U	H	R	J	N	S	B	E	R
I	R	M	H	R	N	R	A	V	A	E	R	A	H	A
S	I	A	I	I	D	I	J	W	R	B	A	D	C	J
M	M	L	M	I	B	A	J	N	U	P	P	I	L	U
I	H	V	M	U	G	H	L	A	I	M	D	A	R	G
I	S	A	H	E	B	I	O	U	D	U	P	I	O	A
S	A	N	E	S	E	M	A	S	S	A	E	I	I
I	K	I	I	N	A	L	A	R	E	K	N	U	K	H

INDIAN CUISINES

ANDHRAN
ASSAMESE
AWADHI
BENGALI
BHOJPURI
BIHARI
CHETTINAD
GOAN
GUJARATI

HYDERABADI
JAIN
KASHMIRI
KERALAN
MALVANI
MUGHLAI
NAGA
ORIYA
PARSI

PUNJABI
RAJASTHANI
SIKKIMESE
SINDHI
TAMIL
TRIPURI
UDUPI

```
L E L D E T I R I P S P E G J
P U Y G U L I V E L Y U E N U
B P F R A P T U R O U S P I U
R H E S C H I R P Y E D F H T
I O E C S T A T I C X E L G N
A R C G N I Z A M A U Y Y U A
N I L C E L L D N R L O I A L
O C U J H L O B I Y T J N L I
G C F D O E R V O I A R G U B
N O R Y E Y E D T Y N E H F U
I N E P D T O R E A T V I Y J
K T D P S A I U F T E O G O U
L E N A I W L C S U A B H J X
A N O H C I O G X I L L P E W
W T W T H R I L L E D E E U Z
```

FEELING GREAT

AMAZING
BLISSFUL
CHEERFUL
CHIRPY
CONTENT
ECSTATIC
ELATED
EUPHORIC
EXCITED

EXULTANT
FLYING HIGH
GLAD
HAPPY
JOYFUL
JOYOUS
JUBILANT
LAUGHING
LIVELY

OVERJOYED
RAPTUROUS
SPIRITED
THRILLED
UPBEAT
WALKING ON AIR
WONDERFUL

L	H	L	A	P	E	L	P	I	N	S	R	E	E	A
R	A	O	B	R	E	H	T	A	E	F	O	T	R	L
N	I	P	R	A	L	L	O	C	S	S	T	R	F	L
C	R	R	E	N	N	E	E	P	R	E	C	K	E	E
A	N	C	A	S	S	E	O	C	D	G	E	C	I	R
N	E	H	U	R	E	R	A	N	E	A	T	I	H	B
E	T	P	U	F	R	S	U	T	A	S	O	T	C	M
W	E	P	P	A	F	B	S	K	A	R	R	S	R	U
A	L	P	N	I	R	L	L	A	E	O	P	G	E	T
T	K	H	H	E	L	F	I	V	L	C	T	N	K	E
C	N	S	M	H	A	C	O	N	P	G	E	I	D	L
H	A	M	K	N	O	L	E	R	K	E	K	K	N	L
S	U	I	E	R	G	P	A	I	N	S	C	L	A	A
C	R	T	K	C	A	P	C	E	T	E	O	A	H	W
A	N	D	N	A	B	M	R	A	R	I	P	W	L	H

CLOTHING ACCESSORIES

ANKLET
ARMBAND
CANE
CAP
COLLAR PIN
CORSAGE
CUFFLINKS
CUMMERBUND

FAN
FEATHER BOA
GLASSES
GLOVE
HAIRNET
HANDKERCHIEF
LAPEL PIN
POCKET PROTECTOR

PURSE
SASH
SPORRAN
TIE CLIP
UMBRELLA
WALKING STICK
WALLET
WATCH

C	O	M	P	T	O	N	C	I	T	N	A	L	T	A
T	W	F	D	W	A	S	O	P	I	R	A	M	S	D
E	A	O	O	W	R	A	R	A	R	T	E	S	I	A
E	H	S	N	E	H	T	A	T	N	O	M	R	E	V
R	S	N	O	T	G	N	I	H	S	A	W	O	E	F
T	N	N	C	L	A	D	C	D	S	S	D	C	A	
S	E	A	N	A	N	E	H	O	L	O	E	N	N	R
W	R	S	K	A	L	I	C	A	T	L	N	U	E	M
O	C	E	I	A	N	I	U	O	R	A	L	G	R	D
L	N	D	M	A	P	S	O	G	P	A	C	E	O	A
L	N	O	T	W	O	L	D	R	A	W	M	S	L	L
I	R	O	E	N	O	T	S	E	R	I	F	L	F	E
W	W	A	L	L	I	V	A	R	A	M	E	E	E	R
N	P	D	O	U	G	L	A	S	F	N	A	D	G	D
J	E	F	F	E	R	S	O	N	U	S	C	D	U	E

LOS ANGELES METRO RAIL STATIONS

ALLEN
ARTESIA
ATLANTIC
CHINATOWN
COMPTON
CRENSHAW
DEL AMO
DEL MAR
DOUGLAS

EL SEGUNDO
FARMDALE
FIRESTONE
FLORENCE
INDIANA
JEFFERSON/USC
LAKE
MARAVILLA
MARIPOSA

PICO
SLAUSON
SOTO
VERMONT ATHENS
WARDLOW
WASHINGTON
WILLOW STREET

R	N	K	T	H	O	R	O	U	G	H	B	R	E	D
I	R	A	L	N	O	R	E	H	C	R	E	P	R	I
C	T	I	G	A	O	C	O	S	A	L	E	R	N	O
L	J	O	Z	R	D	B	R	E	T	O	N	Y	R	F
E	U	U	R	O	O	R	D	I	N	L	B	E	I	O
V	I	C	T	I	K	M	U	A	O	M	L	N	A	T
E	M	A	C	L	C	A	P	B	U	L	N	R	N	N
L	U	L	K	R	A	S	R	R	E	I	L	O	S	I
A	R	A	O	O	I	N	B	U	S	R	D	O	O	P
N	G	B	O	H	L	E	D	H	M	E	R	I	H	S
D	E	R	B	F	L	A	H	H	S	I	D	E	W	S
B	S	E	N	O	N	I	U	S	R	E	L	A	W	S
A	E	S	O	L	D	E	N	B	U	R	G	A	O	I
Y	Z	E	N	O	R	T	H	S	W	E	D	I	S	H
R	O	R	L	O	V	T	R	O	T	T	E	R	M	O

BREEDS OF HORSE

BRETON
BRUMBY
CALABRESE
CLEVELAND BAY
CRIOLLO
DON
FINNISH
HISPANO
JUTLAND

KLADRUBER
LOKAI
MORGAN
MURAKOZ
MURGESE
NONIUS
NORTH SWEDISH
OLDENBURG
ORLOV TROTTER

PERCHERON
PINTO
SALERNO
SHIRE
SWEDISH HALFBRED
THOROUGHBRED
TORIC
WALER

R	E	V	O	L	L	O	R	W	O	L	S	P	R	H
P	M	U	J	L	E	P	N	W	O	D	A	A	L	A
O	E	L	E	S	O	S	L	O	E	W	E	B	O	D
M	O	E	F	I	O	O	S	A	O	D	P	D	N	T
O	H	L	E	T	O	B	B	I	Y	A	A	A	H	I
O	Y	A	T	S	T	B	K	A	K	D	T	S	N	E
R	O	D	C	F	D	A	H	H	K	S	E	I	A	L
R	T	M	H	E	D	N	E	B	D	E	A	A	O	D
U	S	H	A	K	E	T	E	N	K	P	E	E	D	D
O	L	C	S	T	O	L	A	F	R	L	O	P	P	A
Y	D	T	C	U	E	H	A	S	A	L	U	T	E	P
O	E	A	W	O	T	B	N	P	B	I	C	A	S	K
T	G	C	A	P	M	A	E	O	U	E	U	O	I	B
O	U	D	I	G	O	E	S	G	G	P	U	T	E	G
G	H	O	T	O	O	C	H	I	G	H	F	I	V	E

DOG COMMANDS

BARK
BEG
CATCH
COME
DOWN
EAT
FETCH
GET UP
GO TO YOUR ROOM
HANDSTAND

HEEL
HIGH FIVE
HUG
JUMP
KISS
LIE
PADDLE
PAW
PEEKABOO
PLAY DEAD

ROLL OVER
SALUTE
SHAKE
SIT
SLOW
STAY
STOP
WAIT

A	E	C	O	P	A	L	O	E	G	O	B	M	A	G
O	J	G	C	P	O	L	Y	E	S	T	E	R	N	C
G	I	G	A	M	B	I	R	E	N	P	A	G	A	N
E	A	C	A	R	O	I	D	L	O	M	A	L	M	A
N	I	O	Z	N	E	B	R	L	B	L	L	I	P	K
I	R	X	E	M	J	N	Y	E	I	E	O	R	I	E
M	C	A	A	Y	A	M	R	P	H	P	Y	N	G	S
A	A	S	R	E	S	O	S	O	Y	O	T	A	L	R
L	R	A	J	R	Y	T	Y	P	G	P	S	M	G	R
E	A	R	A	H	H	T	A	X	M	N	A	R	U	O
M	N	A	L	P	L	N	S	A	O	S	I	H	M	S
M	N	H	A	L	A	M	S	I	T	P	E	H	M	E
E	A	C	P	X	E	L	E	I	E	L	E	M	I	T
E	P	A	I	N	A	R	C	I	L	O	N	E	H	P
H	N	M	N	B	B	H	A	M	I	N	O	O	T	M

RESINS

ACAROID
AMBER
AMINO
BALSAM
BENZOIN
CARANNA
CHARAS
COPAL
ELEMI

EPOXY
GALIPOT
GAMBIR
GAMBOGE
GUM
HING
JALAPIN
KINO
MASTIC

MELAMINE
MYRRH
OPOPANAX
PHENOLIC
POLYESTER
POLYMER
ROSET
SHELLAC
STYRAX

```
S W R B P H A L A R O P E C E
P R H G K T H R T S I B I U R
E R N I N A O G W I G T R R L
L E L I M L E A U R W E R L K
I H T D L B M L E O H E U E N
C S L E R P R E U C H G E W A
A I R I H I N E T N A C G P H
N F T E M S B A L E I U A L S
R G N E H P C E S I I L I T D
A N T A N R K O T L F A L E E
M I N E E N O I L A R F L A R
L K U T T G A E N A G E U L G
U G S A U K M G O D W I T R K
F Y S P O O N B I L L R F L
O K R O T S E C O O T N L F T
```

WATER AND WADING BIRDS

AUK
CHOUGH
COOT
CURLEW
FRIGATE BIRD
FULMAR
GALLINULE
GANNET
GODWIT
GOOSE

GREENSHANK
GUILLEMOT
IBIS
KINGFISHER
LIMPKIN
OYSTERCATCHER
PEEWIT
PELICAN
PHALAROPE
RAIL

REDSHANK
ROLLER
RUFF
SEAGULL
SPOONBILL
STINT
STORK
SWAMPHEN
TEAL
WHIMBREL

A	M	H	I	O	I	D	R	G	O	B	W	E	R	R
H	L	C	G	R	C	E	N	I	L	I	D	E	R	O
D	H	T	C	O	E	L	D	O	P	R	D	L	E	I
U	F	I	E	H	H	A	U	E	E	K	E	D	T	L
S	R	W	K	R	R	R	R	B	R	S	K	N	E	G
N	O	S	D	C	N	S	E	S	C	T	A	A	M	A
H	N	T	S	A	O	A	O	Y	E	R	R	H	O	U
C	T	H	K	M	S	L	T	D	A	A	B	R	H	G
T	S	G	E	A	D	H	R	O	O	L	T	O	C	E
U	E	I	D	U	A	B	B	O	R	M	P	O	A	L
L	A	L	K	L	N	R	S	O	O	G	E	D	T	A
C	T	D	T	K	C	O	L	C	A	D	A	T	C	C
O	R	A	S	U	N	V	I	S	O	R	H	U	E	C
T	A	E	S	T	E	K	C	U	B	E	D	E	G	R
S	T	H	G	I	L	Y	C	N	E	G	R	E	M	E

DRIVING VEHICLES

ALTERNATOR GAUGE
BRAKE
BUCKET SEAT
CD PLAYER
CLOCK
CLUTCH
DASHBOARD

DOOR HANDLE
DOOR LOCK
EMERGENCY LIGHTS
FRONT SEAT
HEADLIGHT SWITCH
ODOMETER
OIL GAUGE

RADIO
REAR SEAT
SUN VISOR
TACHOMETER
WIPERS

E	L	F	U	G	L	I	S	I	X	A	R	A	P	S
N	T	R	S	A	D	R	N	E	M	A	L	C	Y	C
A	A	I	I	L	S	I	L	L	Y	R	A	M	A	H
A	I	T	N	T	B	S	G	L	A	D	I	O	L	I
A	T	I	Y	O	S	N	O	W	D	R	O	P	L	N
C	E	L	L	N	C	U	I	A	W	N	M	I	A	C
I	R	L	I	I	N	A	G	P	E	I	U	I	M	H
D	B	A	L	A	S	A	R	R	I	Q	R	X	E	E
A	T	R	S	A	R	C	I	E	N	L	W	I	N	R
N	N	Y	L	L	G	N	I	O	T	A	U	A	O	I
T	O	A	I	I	E	C	J	L	O	N	E	T	M	N
H	M	C	B	L	U	E	B	E	L	L	I	P	E	C
E	C	R	O	C	O	S	M	I	A	A	R	W	N	H
R	R	T	D	S	U	S	S	I	C	R	A	N	A	E
A	H	S	U	C	O	R	C	N	M	U	T	U	A	E

PLANT BULBS

ACIDANTHERA
AMARYLLIS
ANEMONE
AUTUMN CROCUS
BLUEBELL
CHINCHERINCHEE
CROCOSMIA
CYCLAMEN

FRITILLARY
GALTONIA
GARLIC
GLADIOLI
IRIS
IXIA
JONQUIL
LILY

MONTBRETIA
NARCISSUS
NERINE
SCILLA
SNOWDROP
SPARAXIS
TULIP
WINTER ACONITE

N	A	S	H	E	P	A	T	R	O	C	L	U	S	U
J	S	E	E	P	A	M	U	C	Y	C	L	O	P	S
P	I	L	C	O	I	S	E	L	U	C	R	E	H	N
E	C	L	T	L	A	E	T	H	E	S	E	U	S	O
R	A	I	O	E	P	T	O	C	A	D	M	U	S	N
S	R	H	R	N	S	E	N	D	P	S	O	U	R	M
E	U	C	M	E	D	U	S	A	Y	R	C	R	O	E
U	S	A	E	P	U	I	Y	C	L	S	I	U	E	M
S	D	I	O	M	E	D	E	S	S	A	S	A	A	A
S	S	T	U	A	N	O	G	R	A	I	T	E	M	G
A	T	E	L	E	M	A	C	H	U	S	R	A	U	A
A	B	E	L	L	E	R	O	P	H	O	N	E	D	S
J	I	E	A	J	A	S	O	N	R	J	U	L	N	E
A	H	R	S	I	E	S	I	R	B	U	Y	U	M	S
X	R	D	N	A	R	C	I	S	S	U	S	A	N	O

GREEK MYTHOLOGICAL CHARACTERS

ACHILLES
AGAMEMNON
AJAX
ARGONAUTS
ATALANTA
BELLEROPHON
BRISEIS
CADMUS
CYCLOPS

DIOMEDES
HECTOR
HELEN
HERCULES
ICARUS
JASON
MEDUSA
NARCISSUS
ODYSSEUS

PATROCLUS
PENELOPE
PERSEUS
PRIAM
SIRENS
TELEMACHUS
THESEUS

```
Y  T  A  L  U  O  G  U  O  Y  A  B  K  Z  G
P  U  C  F  R  E  M  O  N  T  A  I  I  E  C
I  A  K  A  I  I  C  A  D  Z  E  A  C  H  A
A  A  T  I  I  K  Q  H  T  E  U  D  H  C  L
N  A  H  A  A  A  U  E  A  A  N  A  T  U
K  U  P  S  T  D  P  N  I  R  C  D  I  A  S
A  P  A  A  A  A  I  A  A  L  O  A  O  N  A
S  I  T  A  I  L  V  E  L  B  E  K  U  S  I
H  L  I  C  A  F  U  I  N  A  A  U  E  G  E
A  A  T  O  G  T  O  G  U  O  U  W  T  E  O
W  L  I  A  D  I  A  H  U  M  P  H  H  E  J
T  U  A  Y  A  Z  O  O  S  M  O  C  I  T  A
E  T  I  U  N  I  L  K  O  W  A  S  A  I  V
T  K  C  O  N  N  A  H  A  P  P  A  R  L  A
H  U  M  A  T  I  L  L  A  E  Y  A  K  N  N
```

NATIVE AMERICAN TRIBES

APACHE
BAYOUGOULA
CALUSA
CHEROKEE
DEADOSE
EYAK
FREMONT
GUACATA
HAIDA
HUALAPAI

ICAFUI
INUIT
KICHAI
MUGULASHA
NATCHEZ
NAVAJO
OCITA
ONEIDA
PATITI
PIANKASHAW

QUILEUTE
RAPPAHANNOCK
SAWOKLI
TATAVIUM
TULALIP
UMATILLA
WABANAKI
YAZOO
YUKI
ZUNI

A	L	C	L	M	U	I	Z	E	P	A	R	T	L	O
E	E	Q	L	O	C	T	A	G	O	N	R	A	E	R
S	P	E	N	T	A	G	O	N	I	I	V	L	P	N
P	Q	N	O	G	A	X	E	H	A	O	C	S	A	M
I	S	U	E	O	D	N	N	N	D	R	G	S	R	L
L	R	M	A	G	T	D	G	L	I	G	L	U	A	R
L	E	E	U	R	N	L	L	C	R	O	R	B	L	A
E	A	A	C	O	E	K	I	T	E	E	E	M	L	T
P	M	N	M	T	A	R	P	E	D	E	H	O	E	S
U	Y	A	C	T	A	Y	L	N	E	C	E	H	L	E
O	I	R	M	O	G	N	I	E	N	T	A	R	O	O
D	M	O	A	D	N	L	G	N	G	I	R	L	G	G
L	O	A	D	M	Y	E	I	L	O	D	T	P	R	C
I	P	R	E	C	I	A	I	A	E	Y	E	N	A	E
E	R	E	H	P	S	D	G	G	R	G	A	W	M	U

SHAPES

CIRCLE	KITE	RHOMBUS
CONE	OCTAGON	SPHERE
CYLINDER	OVAL	SQUARE
DIAMOND	PARALLELOGRAM	STAR
ELLIPSE	PENTAGON	TRAPEZIUM
HEART	PYRAMID	TRIANGLE
HEXAGON	RECTANGLE	WEDGE

R	K	S	O	E	H	O	L	O	C	R	I	N	E	Y
O	T	L	A	P	N	P	C	A	S	K	S	U	M	N
I	V	A	I	E	I	D	M	S	U	C	U	M	H	E
M	A	A	E	S	R	N	O	Y	A	P	M	I	Y	C
L	V	T	R	W	L	C	E	C	L	E	Y	I	P	T
A	S	R	T	Y	S	I	N	A	R	U	H	L	O	A
N	D	I	G	R	E	E	N	A	L	I	T	I	P	R
E	I	T	O	N	S	I	L	G	P	D	N	V	H	Y
R	G	L	I	O	A	P	O	C	R	I	N	E	Y	M
A	E	N	I	R	C	O	X	E	E	T	C	R	S	A
R	S	C	I	C	A	R	O	H	T	O	R	P	I	M
P	T	D	I	O	R	Y	H	T	A	R	A	P	S	M
U	I	E	N	I	R	C	C	E	R	A	I	O	T	A
S	V	Y	R	A	V	I	L	A	S	P	L	C	E	R
L	E	A	L	A	I	G	Y	P	O	R	U	E	I	Y

GLANDS

APOCRINE
DIGESTIVE
ECCRINE
ENDOCRINE
EXOCRINE
GREEN
HOLOCRINE
HYPOPHYSIS
LIVER
LYMPH

MAMMARY
MUCUS
MUSK-SAC
NECTARY
OIL
OVARY
PANCREAS
PARATHYROID
PAROTID
PINEAL

PROTHORACIC
SALIVARY
SILK
SUPRARENAL
SWEAT
THYMUS
TONSIL
UROPYGIAL

I	B	L	I	M	B	O	L	E	R	O	K	T	W	A
R	A	B	M	A	S	C	O	T	K	B	A	N	A	A
I	P	A	S	O	D	O	B	L	E	R	O	W	L	N
S	E	R	D	I	S	C	O	K	A	T	N	O	T	E
H	T	A	O	T	A	C	B	N	S	G	A	T	Z	R
T	S	R	T	S	I	W	T	E	S	M	O	R	L	A
A	K	G	N	B	K	E	L	O	L	G	A	O	M	C
C	C	N	L	P	L	R	S	K	N	L	T	M	B	A
A	I	A	B	L	A	P	E	A	O	I	Y	G	B	M
N	U	H	A	H	Y	N	T	E	A	B	M	U	R	O
C	Q	B	C	L	N	T	O	R	T	X	O	F	O	C
A	L	W	A	M	G	U	B	R	E	T	T	I	J
N	H	C	M	E	R	E	N	G	U	E	N	R	S	R
L	L	O	R	D	N	A	K	C	O	R	R	B	C	L
O	E	R	O	L	A	M	B	E	T	H	W	A	L	K

DANCES

BALLET
BELLY
BHANGRA
BOLERO
BOOGALOO
BREAK
CALYPSO
CANCAN
CHARLESTON

DISCO
FOXTROT
IRISH
JITTERBUG
LAMBETH WALK
LIMBO
MACARENA
MAMBO
MERENGUE

PASO DOBLE
QUICKSTEP
ROCK AND ROLL
RUMBA
SAMBA
TANGO
TARANTELLA
TWIST
WALTZ

F	L	C	A	U	G	U	S	T	I	N	E	E	R	D
O	U	R	L	A	D	Y	O	F	L	O	R	E	T	O
A	C	S	A	E	C	O	O	V	I	R	H	H	A	T
N	Y	A	T	E	E	S	P	D	E	M	O	R	E	J
G	R	N	I	J	C	Y	E	D	I	M	O	H	Y	S
E	H	I	Z	O	I	R	S	B	A	N	O	A	N	I
L	O	U	E	S	L	A	L	S	A	M	A	A	M	S
I	N	Q	K	E	I	M	M	I	O	S	I	O	I	U
C	O	A	U	P	A	O	R	B	E	N	T	S	J	I
O	R	S	L	H	R	P	O	R	I	G	I	I	J	S
A	A	A	O	E	Y	N	A	P	S	D	R	A	A	E
N	T	M	S	C	U	S	S	U	O	U	D	O	M	N
N	U	O	Y	S	M	I	B	R	L	A	T	A	E	E
E	S	H	P	U	R	N	E	H	M	A	I	I	S	G
E	A	T	S	C	W	E	R	D	N	A	M	A	V	E

PATRON SAINTS

ADAM	GENESIUS	LUCY
AMAND	GEORGE	LUKE
ANDREW	HOMOBONUS	MARY
ANGELICO	HONORATUS	OUR LADY OF LORETO
ANNE	ISIDORE	PAULA
AUGUSTINE	IVO	SEBASTIAN
CECILIA	JAMES	THOMAS AQUINAS
CRISPINIAN	JEROME	THOMAS MORE
CYPRIAN	JOAN	VITUS
ERASMUS	JOSEPH	ZITA

152

K	M	E	E	M	A	G	E	V	O	L	T	R	R	P
R	I	S	E	D	T	S	U	T	E	R	I	P	M	U
A	X	E	K	L	O	C	E	M	H	S	A	T	P	U
P	E	R	T	E	H	H	D	R	E	I	O	N	S	I
E	D	V	R	T	S	I	L	L	V	H	R	O	E	E
N	D	I	U	T	G	P	G	O	H	E	P	T	C	U
R	O	C	O	O	N	N	W	S	B	E	R	U	Y	E
U	U	E	C	H	I	R	A	I	N	D	E	L	A	Y
O	B	L	D	S	S	M	M	P	L	D	A	E	R	D
B	L	I	R	P	S	I	E	L	U	D	I	A	L	R
L	E	N	A	O	A	N	I	P	S	K	C	A	B	I
E	S	E	H	R	P	D	N	A	H	K	C	A	B	V
M	E	N	S	D	O	U	B	L	E	S	S	O	R	E
I	O	C	E	C	I	L	S	T	P	U	T	O	N	D
Y	L	L	A	R	C	L	A	Y	C	O	U	R	T	K

GAME OF TENNIS

ATP	LET	RALLY
BACKHAND	LOB	SERVER
BACKSPIN	LOVE GAME	SERVICE LINE
CHIP	MELBOURNE PARK	SINGLES
CLAY COURT	MENS DOUBLES	SLICE
DEUCE	MIXED DOUBLES	SMASH
DRIVE	NOT UP	THIRTY
DROP SHOT	PASSING SHOT	UMPIRE
HARD COURT	RACKET	US OPEN
KNOCK UP	RAIN DELAY	WILD CARD

R	H	S	P	S	S	O	R	T	A	B	L	A	T	P
R	E	T	A	W	R	A	E	H	S	E	A	M	E	W
E	R	O	R	E	U	P	A	K	A	T	L	E	F	R
H	R	R	A	I	V	O	R	Y	G	U	L	L	U	O
C	I	M	Z	E	F	I	W	D	L	O	U	V	L	E
T	N	Y	O	Y	K	Y	B	O	O	B	G	D	M	T
A	G	P	R	C	E	I	E	R	A	A	S	E	A	E
C	G	E	B	O	T	C	T	P	A	Q	U	P	R	L
R	U	T	I	O	U	I	A	T	U	R	O	R	R	K
E	L	R	L	T	C	C	T	A	I	U	C	I	G	U
T	L	E	L	A	K	A	W	I	E	W	U	O	A	A
S	U	L	C	C	T	A	E	T	R	H	A	N	N	A
Y	S	E	A	D	U	C	K	S	N	I	L	K	N	K
O	B	L	U	E	S	H	A	G	E	O	G	A	E	E
S	B	L	U	P	E	N	G	U	I	N	C	R	T	A

SEABIRDS

ALBATROSS
AUKLET
BLACKCAP
BLUE SHAG
BOOBY
COOT
ERNE
FULMAR
GANNET

GLAUCOUS GULL
HERRING GULL
IVORY GULL
KITTIWAKE
OLD SQUAW
OLDWIFE
OYSTERCATCHER
PENGUIN
PRION

RAZORBILL
SEA COB
SEA DUCK
SEA MEW
SHEARWATER
STORMY PETREL
TAKAPU
TITI

G N I D I R E S R O H R I M T
E T I S N A V A R A C A G D I
M C Y C L E T R A I L A E A A
W W I N D P U M P S L O Y R E
L N B E A C O N I T H A M T T
E T I S C I N C I P W O I G N
B T E L T S A C B P O S M A I
O L I O T D M O I R P U S L O
A S E P I C A L I M E G G L P
T M L A L T S N A S O N N E W
H A A O T E G C U I M I I R E
I S C R P S V M B R I K H Y I
R T I U S E R A Y S M R S T V
E P W A L K S O R T R A I L S
S L L I M D N I W G Y P F P T

MAP FEATURES

ART GALLERY
BEACON
BOAT HIRE
BOAT TRIPS
CAMP SITE
CARAVAN SITE
CASTLE
CYCLE TRAIL

FISHING
GRAVEL PIT
HORSE RIDING
MAST
MOORINGS
MUSEUM
PARKING
PICNIC SITE

SLIPWAY
SLOPES
VIEWPOINT
WALKS OR TRAILS
WINDMILL
WIND PUMP

M	O	T	H	E	R	I	N	L	A	W	G	G	D	H
D	R	A	W	E	D	C	M	D	A	D	D	O	O	T
L	E	G	T	I	R	N	E	P	H	E	W	D	R	N
I	T	L	H	F	F	T	A	N	N	S	A	M	E	E
H	H	R	C	I	A	E	N	B	I	I	S	O	H	R
C	G	E	U	N	T	H	C	U	S	E	T	T	T	A
D	U	T	R	L	U	O	O	L	A	U	C	H	O	P
O	A	S	E	G	N	I	L	B	I	S	H	E	R	R
G	D	I	N	N	C	O	U	S	I	N	N	R	B	E
O	D	S	G	T	G	R	A	N	D	S	O	N	F	T
D	O	T	W	I	N	B	R	O	T	H	E	R	L	S
S	G	G	R	A	N	D	F	A	T	H	E	R	A	O
O	D	D	L	I	H	C	R	E	T	S	O	F	H	F
N	D	D	G	N	S	G	O	D	F	A	T	H	E	R
R	E	T	H	G	U	A	D	D	N	A	R	G	I	T

RELATIVES

AUNT
COUSIN
DAD
FOSTER-CHILD
FOSTER-PARENT
GODCHILD
GODDAUGHTER
GODFATHER

GODMOTHER
GODSON
GRANDDAUGHTER
GRANDFATHER
GRANDSON
HALF-BROTHER
HUSBAND
MOTHER-IN-LAW

NEPHEW
NIECE
SIBLING
SISTER
TWIN BROTHER
UNCLE
WIFE

```
C O T T O N T A I L W L L L E
G H O S T W H I T E L R L W K
F T M N I W M H L E P E E L L
L V A O M M M A H L H H I O E
O A G W O L E S G S F S D C B
R N E N I L G T A N N L A D Y
A I E U R G E E I R O L A R U
L L W R E T S S O H D L O X T
W L C C E Y W C E L W V I L I
H A R E E A T L O A I T M A N
I H E T I H W E U Q I T N A J
T C A V V L R A E P D E E S C
E N M C H A M P A G N E R S A
B E I G E T I H W O J A V A N
T O S A E T I H W H C T U D G
```

SHADES OF WHITE

ANTIQUE WHITE
BEIGE
CHAMPAGNE
CORNSILK
COTTONTAIL
CREAM
DUTCH WHITE
ECRU

EGGSHELL
FLAX
FLORAL WHITE
GHOST WHITE
IVORY
LINEN
MAGNOLIA
NAVAJO WHITE

OLD LACE
SEASHELL
SEED PEARL
SNOW
VANILLA
WHITE MIST

FICTIONAL DOCTORS

BASHIR
COCKROACH
COX
CRUSHER
CYCLOPS
DOLITTLE
EMMETT BROWN
EVIL
FAUSTUS

FRANK-N-FURTER
FU MANCHU
GRISSOM
HIBBERT
HIGGINS
HOLLYWOOD
HOUSE
JACK STAPLETON
JEKYLL

MARTIN
QUINCY
QUINN
ROSS GELLER
SCULLY
TEETH
WATSON
WHO
ZHIVAGO

P	I	P	E	H	Y	A	W	R	I	A	F	I	A	O
H	C	T	I	D	H	Y	A	W	L	L	I	P	S	O
A	Q	U	E	D	U	C	T	O	S	L	U	I	C	E
E	W	O	L	F	R	E	V	O	F	Y	F	C	L	Y
L	L	L	U	V	T	A	L	S	A	U	W	E	T	L
G	U	L	L	Y	E	A	U	W	F	H	G	S	I	I
A	E	B	U	T	A	R	R	C	G	R	D	R	U	E
S	I	P	H	O	N	E	T	U	O	W	O	U	D	T
O	U	E	C	W	T	Y	O	O	D	R	L	O	N	R
S	L	G	T	A	G	R	V	L	E	E	T	C	O	E
F	E	E	W	Y	T	E	C	I	E	T	E	R	C	F
L	T	W	W	O	L	L	O	H	F	T	L	E	A	M
U	L	F	E	N	N	I	A	R	D	U	L	T	N	A
M	I	F	U	R	R	O	W	G	T	G	U	A	A	H
E	W	A	T	E	R	M	A	I	N	Y	G	W	L	C

FOR RUNNING WATER

AQUEDUCT
CANAL
CHAMFER
CONDUIT
CULVERT
DITCH
DRAIN
FAIRWAY
FEED

FLUME
FURROW
GROOVE
GULLET
GULLY
GUTTER
HOLLOW
OVERFLOW
PIPE

SEWER
SIPHON
SLUICE
SPILLWAY
TROUGH
TUBE
WATERCOURSE
WATER MAIN
WATERWAY

```
H M K A J B I H S A Y A B O K
M Y A A T L M S C H M I D T N
A N E S A W O S H H I G G S K
P M I S K K O S T E R L I T Z
E I A T A A M W I N E L A N D
R T V N O T W A M G E I M D N
L B O E O I K A S A K A L L A
M A L J T S S E I R M A H B M
U T E H C O R A H E N N E A B
T I S S S N P E N O E N O R U
T J O I A W N A D S G O N I S
E A V M U R D C E L Y O B S B
R K O R O L M W E I S S E H A
S A N H A A A R U M A K A N Z
M A T H E W T S S E L U O H T
```

NOBEL PRIZE FOR PHYSICS WINNERS

AKASAKI
AMANO
BARISH
BOYLE
ENGLERT
GEIM
HALDANE
HAROCHE
HIGGS

KAJITA
KAO
KOBAYASHI
KOSTERLITZ
MASKAWA
MCDONALD
NAKAMURA
NAMBU
NOVOSELOV

PERLMUTTER
RIESS
SCHMIDT
SMITH
THORNE
THOULESS
WEISS
WINELAND

E	N	I	M	S	A	J	S	S	E	C	N	I	R	P
R	L	O	H	T	R	O	W	S	G	O	C	C	O	H
A	K	H	E	R	C	U	L	E	S	I	Y	D	A	L
C	O	N	O	D	O	M	I	S	A	U	Q	N	M	E
S	O	E	F	P	A	B	M	I	S	H	B	A	A	I
E	H	B	R	E	R	R	A	B	B	I	T	Z	S	N
T	N	M	T	T	I	E	A	O	I	S	I	R	T	E
I	I	U	I	E	G	D	S	S	M	L	C	A	E	G
H	A	F	M	R	A	U	M	O	L	U	G	T	J	P
W	T	A	O	P	S	M	O	T	P	E	L	W	M	O
W	P	S	N	A	T	B	A	U	S	A	A	A	O	H
O	A	A	G	N	O	O	N	L	R	M	R	B	N	M
N	C	E	A	O	N	M	A	P	A	T	E	O	U	F
S	P	M	A	U	I	E	C	I	L	A	I	E	U	E
C	R	U	E	L	L	A	D	E	V	I	L	A	T	W

DISNEY ANIMATED CHARACTERS

ABU
ALICE
BRER RABBIT
CAPTAIN HOOK
COGSWORTH
CRUELLA DE VIL
DUMBO
ELSA
GASTON
GENIE

HERCULES
JETSAM
LADY
MAUI
MOANA
MOWGLI
MUFASA
MULAN
PEGASUS
PETER PAN

PLUTO
PRINCESS JASMINE
QUASIMODO
SCAR
SIMBA
SMEE
SNOW WHITE
TARZAN
TIMON
TRAMP

A	E	T	I	L	C	A	G	E	M	N	E	A	T	A
N	I	E	B	E	H	T	I	H	L	S	E	P	E	O
A	E	E	A	A	K	O	P	R	A	C	T	O	U	P
N	I	A	M	E	A	I	L	A	M	I	H	R	A	A
K	R	A	E	E	H	G	D	Y	H	I	E	U	N	S
E	O	O	E	I	T	T	A	I	S	E	A	E	T	I
S	P	T	R	T	E	S	L	N	X	I	L	D	H	P
P	U	O	S	T	S	O	A	A	Y	A	T	I	E	H
O	E	M	N	I	H	A	N	C	M	M	R	H	K	A
N	S	I	R	I	M	O	R	I	O	A	E	P	E	E
D	M	A	U	S	S	E	S	D	X	I	A	D	A	A
E	O	N	O	T	U	A	H	I	A	L	R	D	E	E
S	I	T	E	M	Y	E	M	T	E	E	E	T	E	E
E	E	E	E	M	A	A	R	A	L	E	O	H	M	L
C	A	R	M	E	E	O	C	A	L	L	I	S	T	O

MOONS OF JUPITER

ADRASTEA
AMALTHEA
ANANKE
AUTONOE
CALLISTO
CARME
CARPO
ELARA
EUANTHE
EUPORIE

EUROPA
GANYMEDE
HELIKE
HIMALIA
IOCASTE
LEDA
LYSITHEA
MEGACLITE
METIS
MNEME

ORTHOSIE
PASIPHAE
PRAXIDIKE
SINOPE
SPONDE
THEBE
THELXINOE
THEMISTO

L	X	E	T	N	C	U	T	T	L	E	F	I	S	H
X	L	A	L	A	O	W	S	H	I	P	W	O	R	M
L	E	E	R	K	N	T	U	W	C	L	Q	O	A	S
L	G	R	H	G	N	O	I	H	S	B	U	B	Z	Q
S	O	L	U	S	O	I	A	R	R	U	A	R	O	U
U	H	B	E	M	K	N	W	G	T	L	H	U	R	I
P	O	I	S	S	K	R	A	I	E	L	O	T	S	D
O	C	Y	U	T	N	P	A	U	R	A	G	E	C	I
T	N	T	B	O	E	E	P	S	T	E	A	A	S	M
C	C	O	W	R	Y	R	T	G	C	L	P	O	Y	Q
O	P	O	U	L	P	E	E	C	E	L	L	A	F	K
A	A	D	O	P	O	S	I	M	E	E	I	P	I	L
O	C	H	I	T	O	N	O	L	N	P	L	O	I	E
L	U	A	P	L	M	N	O	R	O	C	L	A	M	H
R	D	O	P	O	T	A	M	O	T	S	I	T	T	W

SHELLFISH

ARGONAUT
ARK SHELL
BULLA
CHANK
CHITON
CLAM
CLIO
COHOG
COWRY
CUTTLEFISH

GAPER
ISOPODA
LOBSTER
MUREX
MYA
OCTOPUS
PECTEN
PERIWINKLE
POULPE
QUAHOG

RAZOR
SEA LEMON
SHIPWORM
SOLEN
SQUID
STOMATOPOD
TRITON
TURBO
TUSK
WHELK

E	R	R	E	G	A	R	E	V	A	E	V	R	U	C
F	O	T	U	O	N	O	I	T	C	A	R	F	A	T
O	S	C	E	A	L	O	B	A	R	A	P	L	L	I
O	I	U	M	A	D	N	U	O	B	D	C	I	M	G
R	V	D	A	V	X	F	O	R	M	U	L	A	H	I
P	I	O	T	M	R	I	F	R	L	M	T	Y	T	D
E	D	R	R	I	D	A	S	A	T	U	S	T	I	G
A	X	P	I	O	C	M	T	N	R	M	L	I	R	E
N	O	P	X	T	A	I	E	O	E	I	A	N	A	O
G	N	P	O	X	O	I	V	I	T	N	U	I	G	M
L	L	R	I	N	T	A	E	T	E	I	Q	F	O	E
E	S	M	O	O	E	A	N	I	M	M	E	N	L	T
C	U	O	U	R	I	N	X	D	A	T	I	I	T	R
M	D	Q	N	C	E	R	T	D	I	U	T	N	R	Y
D	H	P	A	R	G	Z	E	A	D	T	I	M	I	L

MATHEMATICS

ADDITION	EQUALS	LOGARITHM
ANGLE	EVEN	MATRIX
AVERAGE	EXPONENT	MAXIMUM
AXIS	FACTOR	MINIMUM
BOUND	FORMULA	ODD
CALCULATION	FRACTION	PARABOLA
CURVE	GEOMETRY	PRODUCT
DIAMETER	GRAPH	PROOF
DIGIT	INFINITY	QUOTIENT
DIVISOR	LIMIT	ZERO

L	S	R	A	E	H	S	G	N	I	K	N	I	P	O
D	I	C	H	O	P	P	E	R	S	S	R	P	E	B
E	R	T	W	A	S	G	I	J	O	E	K	E	L	R
M	D	O	R	A	Z	O	R	K	W	O	S	V	K	E
H	S	A	W	E	L	E	S	O	O	O	L	A	C	M
E	C	M	L	S	B	C	M	H	E	S	W	H	I	M
L	H	A	R	B	A	N	L	F	K	A	A	S	S	I
O	I	C	S	L	W	L	I	A	S	I	E	E	K	R
P	S	H	P	A	I	N	D	K	N	E	H	K	W	T
P	E	E	L	B	K	Z	C	S	M	N	T	O	A	E
E	L	T	A	K	E	A	A	E	I	A	Y	P	S	G
R	T	E	C	I	H	W	I	S	G	L	C	S	T	D
E	F	I	N	K	T	E	K	C	O	P	S	P	E	E
S	L	P	E	N	K	N	I	F	E	A	M	E	R	H
F	S	W	I	S	S	A	R	M	Y	K	N	I	F	E

GOOD FOR CUTTING

ADZE
BILLHOOK
BLADE
CHAINSAW
CHISEL
CHOPPER
FLICK-KNIFE
FRETSAW
HACKSAW

HEDGE TRIMMER
JIGSAW
LAWNMOWER
LOPPER
MACHETE
PENKNIFE
PINKING SHEARS
PLANE
POCKET KNIFE

RAZOR
SCALPEL
SCYTHE
SICKLE
SPOKESHAVE
SWISS ARMY KNIFE
SWORD

HOMOGRAPHS

BACK
BAT
CONDUCT
COOL
DEAR
DEFECT
DISCHARGE
FINE
FOOT
LEAD

LIGHT
MATCH
MIND
MINUTE
NOVEL
PARK
PERFECT
PROJECT
RETARD
ROCK

SECOND
SEWER
SIGN
SINK
SPIRIT
TEAR
UNIONIZED
WAVE
WELL

```
E  A  H  A  N  D  L  I  N  G  N  A  N  S  D
N  O  I  T  A  R  G  I  M  M  I  O  T  S  H
B  O  D  Y  S  C  A  N  N  E  R  N  R  T  X
I  N  S  P  E  C  T  I  O  N  A  K  Q  N  R
E  G  A  G  G  U  L  A  I  R  A  U  A  E  A
E  C  U  S  T  O  M  S  U  C  A  R  D  M  Y
U  P  T  D  O  O  F  A  P  R  R  U  E  E  M
E  T  E  R  A  R  T  A  A  I  T  L  P  C  A
U  H  K  E  Y  S  S  N  V  Y  O  C  A  N  C
Q  G  C  N  E  S  T  A  F  U  H  T  R  U  H
K  I  I  R  P  I  L  R  N  E  C  E  T  O  I
A  L  T  O  N  S  E  G  C  A  O  I  U  N  N
E  F  R  E  T  E  E  K  N  A  G  D  R  N  E
G  T  A  T  Y  T  I  R  U  C  E  S  E  A  N
S  A  I  U  Q  N  E  N  A  L  P  N  S  S  T
```

AT THE AIRPORT

ANNOUNCEMENTS
ARRIVALS
BODY SCANNER
CHECK-IN
CUSTOMS
DEPARTURES
DUTY FREE
FLIGHT

FOOD
HANDLING
IMMIGRATION
INSPECTION
LOUNGE
LUGGAGE
PASSPORTS
PLANE

QUARANTINE
QUEUE
RESTAURANTS
SECURITY
TICKET
X-RAY MACHINE

O	S	O	T	I	H	O	T	A	S	I	H	T	A	U
T	S	U	G	U	H	I	T	O	T	I	H	A	S	A
T	U	R	A	H	A	K	A	T	H	Y	I	T	M	I
O	D	K	A	T	S	U	H	I	T	O	R	U	O	O
T	O	S	H	I	K	O	H	I	T	O	T	Y	T	T
A	O	T	I	H	I	H	S	O	Y	S	I	A	I	I
M	T	O	M	O	H	I	T	O	U	I	H	S	H	H
K	I	R	A	N	O	R	I	H	N	H	F	U	O	U
A	O	C	A	T	I	H	I	A	I	U	T	H	R	R
Z	T	T	H	M	K	T	G	D	S	S	O	I	I	E
U	I	O	O	I	O	A	E	A	H	T	O	T	H	T
H	H	K	I	H	H	H	H	O	T	I	H	O	O	T
I	I	I	O	I	I	I	O	T	I	H	O	T	O	M
T	K	K	T	T	T	T	O	S	A	H	I	T	O
O	A	O	O	O	U	A	O	O	T	I	H	A	Y	A

EMPERORS OF JAPAN

AKIHITO	KAZUHITO	SATOHITO
ASAHITO	KOTOHITO	TAKAHARU
AYAHITO	MICHIHITO	TERUHITO
FUSAHITO	MIHITO	TOMOHITO
HIDEHITO	MOTOHITO	TOOHITO
HIKOHITO	MUTSUHITO	TOSHIKO
HIROHITO	NAGAHITO	TSUGUHITO
HIRONARI	OKIKO	YASUHITO
KATSUHITO	OSAHITO	YOSHIHITO

N	E	N	I	R	A	A	S	F	O	S	T	E	R	M
G	R	E	I	B	M	O	R	C	R	E	B	A	I	Y
E	B	U	R	G	E	S	T	E	O	A	D	L	R	D
H	S	S	R	E	B	M	A	H	C	T	L	A	E	O
R	A	E	L	R	N	C	B	O	I	S	T	B	Y	N
Y	N	H	T	I	E	X	U	O	D	E	L	O	E	A
A	A	A	S	A	B	H	F	G	K	S	P	Y	M	I
T	S	D	G	O	O	E	C	O	R	E	M	D	E	P
F	H	I	G	H	T	C	S	R	W	O	N	E	I	A
A	H	D	F	N	A	N	P	K	A	K	P	T	N	L
I	R	U	T	N	E	V	I	U	I	G	E	I	N	E
T	O	A	R	T	U	E	N	K	G	N	F	A	U	S
F	A	R	R	E	L	L	G	L	C	I	D	M	J	S
K	A	H	N	S	E	V	A	R	G	A	N	I	I	I
M	I	G	M	A	H	N	R	U	B	F	M	L	R	F

ARCHITECTS

ABERCROMBIE	FOWKE	MILLS
ALESSI	GEHRY	NASH
ARCHER	GRAVES	NEUTRA
BOYD	GROPIUS	NIEMEYER
BURGES	HADID	PEI
BURNHAM	KAHN	PIANO
CHAMBERS	KENT	PUGIN
COATES	LEDOUX	SAARINEN
FARRELL	LIBESKIND	SCOTT
FOSTER	MACKINTOSH	VENTURI

FAMOUS RIVERS

AMAZON
BARROW
CAM
CHURCHILL
CONGO
DANUBE
DORDOGNE
GANGES
INDUS
ISIS

JORDAN
LIMPOPO
LITTLE BIGHORN
MEKONG
MOSELLE
NIGER
NILE
ORINOCO
OUSE
RIO GRANDE

SEVERN
TAY
THAMES
TWEED
TYNE
VOLTA
YANGTZE
YUKON

C	O	R	H	A	I	K	U	L	L	M	P	S	M	S
L	L	Y	G	O	L	A	N	A	P	A	D	K	L	A
E	H	E	C	I	T	S	O	R	C	A	C	V	Y	T
R	D	R	D	T	I	T	S	A	E	I	L	E	R	E
E	K	A	C	E	I	E	Y	O	R	O	I	R	I	L
G	R	R	L	G	E	K	L	E	N	N	R	S	C	P
G	O	U	N	L	E	L	M	E	R	N	L	E	T	U
O	M	H	N	P	A	I	A	S	G	R	E	C	C	O
D	A	A	I	A	L	B	R	A	U	Y	R	T	R	C
N	N	C	T	E	P	I	G	R	A	M	T	R	R	U
I	T	E	T	I	A	Y	E	P	I	T	A	P	H	L
D	I	A	P	N	A	G	E	D	O	A	L	P	A	A
Y	C	D	L	A	R	O	T	S	A	P	G	A	S	E
L	A	A	O	R	C	N	A	R	R	A	T	I	V	E
L	H	A	L	L	E	G	O	R	Y	D	R	C	S	A

TYPES OF POETRY

ACROSTIC	EPIC	NARRATIVE
ALLEGORY	EPIGRAM	ODE
ANALOGY	EPITAPH	PASTORAL
BALLADE	HAIKU	ROMANTIC
COUPLET	IDYLL	SONNET
DOGGEREL	LIMERICK	VERSE
ELEGY	LYRIC	

TEACHERS

ADVISER
COACH
DEAN
DON
EDUCATOR
FELLOW
GOVERNESS

HEADMASTER
HOUSEMASTER
INSTRUCTOR
LECTURER
MENTOR
MISTRESS
PRECEPTOR

PRINCIPAL
PROFESSOR
SCHOOLTEACHER
TRAINER
TUTOR

HORSE COATS

S	T	R	A	W	B	E	R	R	Y	R	O	A	N	A
A	U	N	E	T	T	I	B	A	E	L	F	E	S	O
O	N	I	B	L	A	P	I	E	B	A	L	D	E	E
B	T	U	N	T	S	E	H	C	R	E	V	I	L	D
Y	S	D	P	T	A	K	T	N	C	T	U	F	A	T
C	E	A	E	S	T	O	E	O	U	O	E	R	T	A
D	H	O	L	D	I	Y	Y	W	I	D	K	E	D	L
W	C	B	T	E	C	K	A	O	B	B	P	B	A	P
N	T	L	U	N	R	L	T	B	A	A	L	P	P	A
W	H	U	B	R	I	R	A	Y	D	N	L	N	P	L
O	G	E	T	C	R	P	O	Y	I	O	Y	D	L	O
R	I	R	B	N	K	R	S	S	B	L	O	E	E	M
B	L	O	C	R	E	A	M	R	A	A	A	L	A	I
K	C	A	L	B	H	S	L	E	R	A	N	R	B	N
K	C	N	I	B	E	I	M	U	O	E	R	K	N	O

ALBINO
BLACK
BLOOD BAY
BLUE ROAN
BROWN
CLAYBANK
CREAM

DAPPLE
DARK BAY
DUN
FLEA-BITTEN
LIGHT CHESTNUT
LIVER CHESTNUT
MEALY

PALOMINO
PIEBALD
PINTO
SKEWBALD
SORREL
STRAWBERRY ROAN

O	T	T	U	I	C	S	O	R	P	E	I	A	C	B
N	A	S	E	M	R	A	P	A	E	S	N	E	L	A
T	O	A	B	P	R	A	P	A	S	S	I	R	E	C
P	I	L	L	R	I	I	T	C	T	T	C	O	N	I
A	A	R	I	L	U	M	S	S	O	N	N	T	O	A
E	I	N	A	V	E	S	A	O	A	L	A	A	P	B
A	N	C	E	M	E	R	C	L	T	P	R	I	R	A
T	S	O	C	T	I	O	A	H	A	T	A	C	A	T
T	A	L	Z	A	T	S	I	Z	E	S	O	C	C	T
E	L	I	M	L	C	O	U	L	Z	T	L	A	S	A
C	A	V	S	S	A	O	N	A	A	O	T	C	A	Z
N	T	E	A	N	T	C	F	E	S	N	M	A	M	Z
A	A	S	G	O	R	G	O	N	Z	O	L	A	N	I
P	A	T	T	O	C	A	U	Q	C	A	A	T	I	P
C	R	O	S	T	I	N	I	O	T	A	L	E	G	E

ITALIAN FOOD

ACQUACOTTA
ARANCINI
BRUSCHETTA
CACCIATORE
CALZONE
CIABATTA
CROSTINI
FOCACCIA
GELATO

GORGONZOLA
INSALATA
MASCARPONE
MOZZARELLA
OLIVE OIL
OLIVES
PANCETTA
PANETTONE
PARMESAN

PASTA
PESTO
PITA
PIZZA
PROSCIUTTO
RISOTTO
SALAMI
TIRAMISU

E	S	N	A	S	E	I	R	E	S	M	S	I	N	A
N	O	I	T	A	R	E	M	U	N	E	E	I	O	D
N	S	U	B	A	L	L	Y	S	S	S	L	I	N	N
R	D	I	C	T	I	O	N	A	R	Y	C	L	T	E
N	C	I	A	D	T	C	U	B	L	A	H	L	A	G
I	R	O	S	I	V	S	A	D	L	U	E	I	L	A
N	E	I	N	U	O	O	I	S	O	B	D	N	U	R
V	T	H	E	T	R	R	C	L	R	B	U	D	B	E
E	S	O	S	O	E	U	C	A	K	X	L	E	A	G
N	O	E	T	C	A	N	A	A	B	C	E	X	T	I
T	R	A	T	V	S	I	T	S	N	U	E	A	I	S
O	A	O	E	L	B	A	T	S	E	A	L	H	T	T
R	R	L	I	T	E	M	S	I	N	H	M	A	C	E
Y	C	A	L	E	N	D	A	R	S	T	L	R	R
N	R	N	R	Y	B	L	I	S	T	I	N	G	A	Y

LISTS

AGENDA
ALMANAC
CALENDAR
CHECKLIST
CONTENTS
DICTIONARY
DIRECTORY
ENUMERATION

INDEX
INVENTORY
ITEMS
LISTING
REGISTER
ROLL
ROSTER
ROTA

SCHEDULE
SERIES
SYLLABUS
TABLE
TABULATION
TALLY
THESAURUS
VOCABULARY

SILKS

I	S	E	O	U	O	B	A	R	A	M	L	E	S	T
X	O	L	F	R	O	N	R	A	E	N	G	T	A	H
M	P	A	R	C	G	B	O	S	P	R	N	U	F	B
A	E	U	N	H	E	A	E	A	E	O	U	H	O	S
R	N	I	L	I	A	D	N	T	R	C	T	C	U	C
T	K	T	U	U	T	R	A	Z	C	E	N	A	L	H
E	Y	M	S	P	Y	A	U	C	A	M	A	R	A	A
T	N	A	T	R	I	K	S	S	O	A	H	A	R	P
T	T	K	R	U	C	R	A	P	E	R	S	P	D	P
E	U	I	I	N	S	L	E	A	V	E	B	L	O	E
G	S	M	N	E	N	S	Y	N	A	F	F	I	T	Y
R	S	O	G	L	A	L	A	M	O	D	E	T	A	B
O	O	N	Y	L	U	E	L	L	U	T	O	A	M	B
E	R	O	T	A	I	T	O	T	T	O	M	A	N	A
G	E	A	E	S	S	E	H	C	U	D	A	G	A	T

ALAMODE	KINCOB	SCHAPPE
ATLAS	LUSTRING	SHANTUNG
BROCADE	MAKIMONO	SLEAVE
CORN	MARABOU	SURAH
CRAPE	ORGANZA	TABBY
CREPE	OTTOMAN	TASAR
DUCHESSE	PARACHUTE	TIFFANY
FLOX	PRUNELLA	TRAM
FOULARD	PULU	TULLE
GEORGETTE	SATIN	TUSSORE

F	L	A	S	T	C	H	I	L	D	C	W	C	J	B
L	O	P	O	T	S	T	N	O	D	H	R	A	A	A
Y	D	S	E	K	A	T	T	I	T	A	H	W	D	C
A	L	W	C	L	O	S	E	R	Z	D	O	U	E	K
W	C	L	A	R	D	S	E	Y	I	I	M	L	D	I
A	F	H	O	L	E	I	N	M	Y	S	O	U	L	N
Y	J	N	E	D	K	V	C	A	L	E	F	B	H	T
F	N	P	I	E	G	T	E	R	S	G	E	A	N	H
R	A	R	I	Y	S	A	H	F	A	A	H	I	O	E
O	M	L	I	R	R	E	R	I	U	S	K	N	M	S
M	D	E	N	B	G	C	C	T	S	A	H	I	A	A
H	N	G	O	M	R	A	I	A	M	W	A	N	E	D
E	I	N	A	F	I	F	T	A	K	E	A	E	R	D
R	L	A	E	O	U	N	M	E	T	E	A	Y	D	L
E	B	R	L	L	I	G	A	D	G	D	U	D	E	E

SONGS BY AEROSMITH

ANGEL
BACK IN THE SADDLE
BEAUTIFUL
BLIND MAN
CHEESE CAKE
CLOSER
CRASH
CRAZY

CRYIN'
DON'T STOP
DREAM ON
DUDE
FEVER
FLY AWAY FROM HERE
GET A GRIP
HOLE IN MY SOUL

JADED
LAST CHILD
MAMA KIN
RAG DOLL
WALK THIS WAY
WHAT IT TAKES

```
P E R F O R M A T R O P R I A
U I E T A M E X S E R V E N O
A M M M P W H A P P L E I I P
I H A A E O N O T W E N H L P
R C G C O P I P P I N N A A O
C T I B B R I N P H B S S C W
H A C O C O N P C R E I L E E
S W M O I I O U O R L I D N R
O E O K R P O K W D P H K O B
T L U P I T A R A O N O P H O
N P S R D R I D D I O A F P O
I P E O D T L M A B R P N I K
C A P A E I I D I I A N I O T
A I U R O N L E S I R T N E C
M Q I N I M C A M I D A O I O
```

APPLE HARDWARE PRODUCTS

AIRPORT	IPOD MINI	MAGIC MOUSE
APPLE II	IPOD NANO	NEWTON
APPLE WATCH	IPOD TOUCH	PERFORMA
CENTRIS	LASERWRITER	PIPPIN
EMATE	LISA	POWERBOOK
IBOOK	MACBOOK AIR	QUADRA
IMAC	MACBOOK PRO	XSERVE
IPAD AIR	MACINTOSH	
IPHONE	MAC MINI	

R	I	P	L	L	A	N	O	I	T	I	D	A	R	T
A	A	I	T	H	I	R	D	S	T	R	E	A	M	E
G	F	A	T	P	I	S	I	E	D	C	E	F	C	N
N	R	N	A	U	I	S	M	N	F	N	L	L	P	O
I	O	O	C	E	M	I	A	T	R	U	A	O	H	B
W	C	E	S	U	T	L	E	E	T	R	B	S	I	M
S	U	S	R	G	E	P	D	E	I	D	R	S	G	O
N	B	D	A	I	M	O	U	N	R	U	T	A	H	R
R	A	R	X	U	M	C	E	A	W	E	A	B	L	T
E	N	I	R	X	S	T	H	D	F	R	E	E	I	O
T	D	T	W	E	S	T	C	O	A	S	T	L	F	N
S	A	X	O	P	H	O	N	E	U	L	E	B	E	D
E	S	N	A	E	L	R	O	W	E	N	O	U	E	T
W	N	M	E	I	G	O	O	W	E	I	G	O	O	B
N	M	A	I	N	S	T	R	E	A	M	N	D	M	S

JAZZ FORMS

AFRO-CUBAN
BOOGIE-WOOGIE
CLARINET
DIXIELAND
DOUBLE BASS
DRUMS
FLUTE
FREE

HARD BOP
HIGHLIFE
MAINSTREAM
MODERN
NEW ORLEANS
PIANO
RAGTIME
SAXOPHONE

SCAT
THIRDSTREAM
TRADITIONAL
TROMBONE
TRUMPET
WEST COAST
WESTERN SWING

FEELING INADEQUATE

AWKWARD
CLUMSY
DEJECTED
DEPRESSED
DESPONDENT
DISPIRITED
DOWNCAST
GLOOMY

GLUM
ILL-ADVISED
ILL-CHOSEN
ILL-FATED
INAPPROPRIATE
INAPT
LONG-FACED
LUCKLESS

MELANCHOLIC
MOURNFUL
SAD
SORROWFUL
UNFORTUNATE
UNLUCKY
UNSUITABLE
UPSET

I	A	E	R	L	E	T	U	T	E	W	E	I	U	D
M	N	E	B	E	S	E	W	I	E	N	B	O	B	N
I	I	I	Y	V	U	N	O	V	W	V	A	P	E	R
N	B	P	E	E	P	E	W	B	B	T	B	H	C	S
I	P	O	W	L	E	T	S	E	E	D	I	D	A	S
M	B	M	A	S	R	K	I	T	D	U	D	S	E	D
I	I	S	P	O	A	A	E	N	A	S	B	E	D	O
P	S	E	D	I	H	S	S	O	O	T	S	D	P	E
D	P	A	V	T	X	B	U	O	K	E	S	U	I	E
S	D	I	R	O	E	R	D	N	S	A	P	S	E	U
S	R	E	R	O	D	P	E	R	O	S	E	X	E	S
P	O	P	E	T	T	E	E	A	A	S	E	R	E	S
U	S	U	F	W	U	E	D	G	S	E	W	T	K	G
L	A	W	E	K	A	Y	A	K	I	E	I	F	N	I
O	P	V	R	O	A	S	R	A	S	T	I	O	O	G

PALINDROMES

AHA	KAYAK	SEES
BIB	LEVEL	SERES
BOB	MINIM	SEXES
DEED	NOON	SIS
DID	PEEP	STATS
DUD	PEP	TENET
EKE	POP	TIT
EWE	PUP	TOOT
EYE	REFER	TUT
GIG	SAGAS	WOW

GOOD STUFF

ACCEPTABLE	EXCELLENT	GREAT
ADEQUATE	EXCEPTIONAL	NICE
AGREEABLE	FABULOUS	PASSABLE
BRILLIANT	FANTASTIC	PLEASANT
CHEERFUL	FINE	SUPER
COMMENDABLE	FIRST-CLASS	TERRIFIC
ENJOYABLE	FIRST-RATE	WONDERFUL

D	T	H	T	W	O	R	G	D	O	U	T	P	U	T
D	E	O	S	N	T	T	R	O	P	E	R	R	S	D
T	E	A	F	R	C	S	P	M	R	O	O	O	S	E
E	N	B	D	F	E	R	T	E	A	R	D	F	E	L
G	O	R	T	L	E	Y	E	S	N	R	H	I	L	I
D	I	E	S	O	I	R	O	D	O	A	K	T	A	V
U	T	S	A	L	R	N	I	L	I	C	L	E	S	E
B	U	A	L	R	U	G	E	T	P	T	L	T	T	R
N	B	H	A	R	E	F	U	N	D	M	O	A	Y	Y
I	I	C	R	E	M	O	T	S	U	C	E	R	O	H
G	R	R	Y	D	I	K	T	N	E	M	Y	A	P	G
R	T	U	R	R	C	R	I	T	I	C	I	F	E	D
A	S	P	I	O	N	I	N	D	U	S	T	R	Y	U
M	I	M	T	O	O	N	E	M	P	L	O	Y	E	E
I	D	S	A	I	S	S	O	L	E	D	N	A	R	B

IT'S ALL BUSINESS

BRAND
BUDGET
COSTS
CREDITOR
CUSTOMER
DEADLINE
DEBTOR
DEFICIT
DELIVERY
DISTRIBUTION

EMPLOYEE
EMPLOYER
GOAL
GROWTH
INDUSTRY
LOSS
MARGIN
MARKET
OFFER
ORDER

OUTPUT
PAYMENT
PENALTY
PROFIT
PURCHASE
REFUND
REPORT
SALARY
SALES
STOCK

I	F	C	N	A	I	C	I	T	U	A	E	B	T	O
E	A	A	H	B	I	A	N	P	Y	D	B	S	N	C
E	R	R	A	E	L	U	A	U	O	A	I	A	B	T
B	M	K	R	S	F	T	M	C	R	T	M	R	T	S
U	E	T	E	O	P	H	T	B	N	S	O	R	C	I
R	R	P	K	R	R	O	E	E	T	K	E	E	E	T
G	M	R	A	E	R	R	D	F	E	R	P	D	T	N
L	N	I	M	N	O	R	A	R	R	R	I	I	E
A	O	N	H	N	T	R	E	O	P	E	I	T	H	I
R	E	T	C	A	C	T	Y	K	E	T	E	O	C	C
H	G	E	T	L	A	E	T	G	N	I	S	R	R	S
C	R	R	A	P	V	O	D	C	U	A	T	A	A	I
A	U	Y	W	R	L	U	S	I	A	W	B	C	R	N
O	S	A	U	I	J	H	N	A	I	C	I	S	U	M
C	P	S	P	A	S	H	O	E	M	A	K	E	R	T

IT'S A JOB

ACTOR
ARCHITECT
AUTHOR
BAKER
BANKER
BARBER
BEAUTICIAN
BROKER
BURGLAR
CHEF

COACH
CRAFTSMAN
DENTIST
DOCTOR
EDITOR
FARMER
JUDGE
MUSICIAN
NURSE
PILOT

PLANNER
POET
PRIEST
PRINTER
SCIENTIST
SHOEMAKER
SURGEON
SURVEYOR
WAITER
WATCHMAKER

IT'S THE TRUTH

ACCURATE
AUTHENTIC
BLUNT
CLEAR
CLOSE
CORRECT
EXACT
FACTUAL
FAIR
FAITHFUL

FORTHRIGHT
GUILELESS
HONEST
INGENUOUS
LITERAL
METICULOUS
OPEN
PLAIN
PRECISE
RIGOROUS

SIMPLE
SINCERE
SOUND
STRICT
TRUE
TRUTHFUL
UNEQUIVOCAL
UNERRING
VALID
VERACITY

INDOOR SPORTS

BASKETBALL
BILLIARDS
BOXING
CURLING
DARTS
DIVING
FENCING
FIGURE SKATING

HANDBALL
JUDO
POOL
RACQUETBALL
REAL TENNIS
ROLLER HOCKEY
SHOOTING
SNOOKER

SPEED SKATING
SQUASH
SWIMMING
TRAMPOLINE
WATER POLO
WEIGHTLIFTING

E	I	T	W	O	B	C	B	R	R	E	B	O	Z	O
M	U	O	N	E	C	K	T	I	E	A	H	I	R	F
B	N	H	I	N	H	T	O	L	C	K	C	E	N	N
C	S	C	C	M	D	O	E	S	C	C	T	E	E	S
R	T	R	S	I	F	T	T	B	W	R	O	C	W	C
D	O	A	N	C	F	O	O	I	O	S	K	H	A	S
H	C	V	N	E	L	A	N	F	E	E	I	R	N	A
M	K	A	E	E	I	D	M	I	R	T	C	F	R	B
F	A	T	A	E	S	O	T	C	E	A	F	O	E	E
R	B	D	D	O	C	K	H	T	N	R	L	U	L	R
N	M	W	R	R	C	I	I	E	A	A	O	L	F	T
C	L	T	A	A	E	E	T	C	N	E	K	A	F	H
I	I	C	L	F	S	B	S	N	O	E	R	U	A
E	A	B	T	A	S	C	O	T	I	E	F	D	M	L
C	A	F	A	L	L	I	N	G	B	A	N	D	D	C

NECKWEAR

ASCOT
BERTHA
BLACK TIE
BOA
BOW TIE
CARCANET
COMFORTER
CRAVAT

FALLING BAND
FICHU
FOULARD
MADRAS
MUFFLER
NECKCLOTH
NECKERCHIEF
NECKTIE

REBOZO
SCARF
STOCK
STOLE
WHITE TIE
WINDSOR TIE

VISIT TO THE ZOO

AARDVARK
ANTEATER
ARMADILLO
BABOON
BADGER
BEAR
BEAVER
BOBCAT
CAMEL
CHEETAH

COUGAR
CROCODILE
GAZELLE
GORILLA
HYENA
JAGUAR
KANGAROO
LEOPARD
LION
LLAMA

LYNX
OCELOT
OSTRICH
PANDA
PANTHER
SNAKE
TIGER
WALLABY
WOLF
ZEBRA

U	A	R	S	S	A	L	G	T	R	O	P	C	R	B
W	I	N	E	G	L	A	S	S	T	E	E	D	E	L
F	R	U	I	T	B	O	W	L	S	R	I	S	G	W
A	N	J	S	P	T	W	T	S	E	N	R	O	R	O
M	E	K	U	D	B	A	A	A	N	C	E	U	A	B
U	E	R	A	G	T	T	L	E	B	O	H	P	H	T
G	R	O	W	E	I	B	R	P	U	M	C	B	C	R
N	U	F	A	M	O	P	E	A	T	P	T	O	P	E
O	T	C	E	W	L	C	L	L	T	O	I	W	L	S
O	U	D	L	A	S	T	O	T	E	T	P	L	A	S
P	A	S	T	A	B	O	W	L	R	E	L	A	C	E
S	A	E	B	E	A	K	E	R	D	A	L	L	E	D
C	O	F	F	E	E	P	O	T	I	R	A	L	M	T
S	U	G	A	R	B	O	W	L	S	S	M	C	A	R
A	G	N	I	K	E	M	A	R	H	T	S	S	T	E

TABLEWARE

BEAKER
BUTTER DISH
CEREAL BOWL
CHARGER
COFFEE POT
COMPOTE
DEMITASSE
DESSERT BOWL
DINNER PLATE

FORK
FRUIT BOWL
JUG
MUG
PASTA BOWL
PLACE MAT
PLATTER
PORT GLASS
RAMEKIN

SMALL PITCHER
SOUP BOWL
SPOON
SUGAR BOWL
TEACUP
TEAPOT
TUREEN
WINE GLASS

A	S	D	L	T	O	R	I	G	A	M	I	N	U	S
A	T	S	R	G	F	E	N	N	O	S	I	O	L	C
Q	A	G	P	A	Y	I	E	N	K	C	O	E	P	I
U	I	G	I	I	W	R	L	R	C	R	I	T	A	H
E	N	O	I	A	N	I	T	M	I	E	N	S	K	P
Y	E	N	G	D	M	N	N	S	E	E	O	C	R	A
R	D	E	B	T	E	T	I	G	E	N	I	U	O	R
E	G	E	A	A	T	I	A	N	N	P	T	L	W	G
D	L	D	T	C	A	L	L	I	G	R	A	P	H	Y
I	A	L	I	R	L	M	G	H	R	I	M	T	C	F
O	S	E	K	O	W	O	I	C	A	N	I	U	T	R
R	S	W	C	C	O	S	V	T	V	T	N	R	A	E
B	T	O	E	H	R	A	I	E	I	I	A	E	P	S
M	E	R	F	E	K	I	R	K	N	N	I	T	R	C
E	G	K	I	T	H	C	K	S	G	G	L	C	V	O

ARTS AND CRAFTS

ANIMATION
BATIK
CALLIGRAPHY
CLOISONNE
COLLAGE
CROCHET
DRAWING
EMBROIDERY

ENGRAVING
FILM
FRESCO
GRAPHICS
METALWORK
MOSAIC
NEEDLEWORK
ORIGAMI

PATCHWORK
SCREEN-PRINTING
SCULPTURE
SKETCHING
SPINNING
STAINED GLASS
TAPESTRY

R	E	M	E	R	Y	C	O	R	U	N	D	U	M	C
E	D	I	A	S	P	O	R	E	L	S	E	R	E	N
T	A	L	C	E	T	I	R	Y	P	I	T	R	E	E
S	T	E	D	N	E	L	B	H	C	T	I	P	E	T
A	A	E	T	I	R	D	N	E	D	T	R	P	T	I
B	E	T	I	M	O	L	O	D	E	E	O	R	I	E
A	M	A	Z	O	N	I	T	E	T	N	H	O	T	D
L	X	A	G	T	T	I	T	C	I	I	P	C	A	A
A	F	A	C	A	R	I	B	I	N	V	S	K	P	J
Z	T	L	R	I	R	A	P	S	O	I	O	S	A	G
I	O	R	I	O	L	N	U	S	M	L	H	A	R	Y
R	E	U	U	N	B	I	E	Q	I	O	P	L	E	P
C	A	L	C	I	T	E	S	T	L	B	T	T	B	S
O	F	P	Y	R	O	X	E	N	E	L	A	E	M	U
N	E	T	I	T	S	E	L	E	C	N	U	E	U	M

MINERALS

ALABASTER	DOLOMITE	PITCHBLENDE
AMAZONITE	EMERY	PYRITE
APATITE	FLINT	PYROXENE
BORAX	FLUORITE	QUARTZ
CALCITE	GARNET	ROCK SALT
CELESTITE	GYPSUM	SILICA
CERITE	JADEITE	SPAR
CORUNDUM	LIMONITE	TALC
DENDRITE	OLIVINE	UMBER
DIASPORE	PHOSPHORITE	ZIRCON

V	N	R	G	E	E	R	G	N	D	E	C	N	E	F
E	L	E	R	N	S	Y	N	N	S	N	H	K	E	N
G	O	L	B	A	P	O	I	G	N	I	W	T	A	E
E	U	K	O	V	A	G	R	G	D	B	P	A	T	H
T	N	N	I	E	V	R	E	B	N	P	E	S	L	A
A	G	I	T	G	I	A	T	U	L	I	I	N	T	W
B	E	R	A	D	N	S	A	S	U	C	N	R	C	I
L	R	P	P	E	G	S	W	H	S	N	G	U	H	H
E	S	S	B	H	M	O	W	E	R	I	D	A	R	U
S	E	E	R	T	T	I	U	R	F	C	O	N	T	P
S	R	I	A	H	C	R	O	O	D	T	U	O	O	E
R	E	V	I	R	D	O	B	E	Z	A	G	I	B	P
S	U	N	B	A	T	H	I	N	G	B	W	S	G	E
R	A	H	E	R	B	S	F	U	P	L	L	S	C	P
Y	R	E	B	B	U	R	H	S	R	E	W	O	L	F

IN THE GARDEN

BENCH
BUSH
DRIVE
FENCE
FLOWERS
FRUIT TREES
GATE
GAZEBO
GRASS

HEDGE
HERBS
LAWN
LOUNGER
MOWER
OUTDOOR CHAIRS
PATH
PATIO
PAVING

PICNIC TABLE
POND
PRUNING
SHRUBBERY
SPRINKLER
SUNBATHING
VEGETABLES
WATERING

E	R	S	S	U	A	L	C	A	T	N	A	S	A	A
C	R	P	I	E	S	E	V	L	E	F	U	S	R	A
U	S	A	O	O	N	T	S	E	G	S	T	D	C	T
A	E	R	A	R	O	I	U	I	I	N	D	N	I	H
S	S	T	E	L	W	E	F	T	E	O	A	R	C	Y
Y	L	I	M	A	F	T	A	S	T	E	H	R	A	W
R	L	E	R	S	S	E	E	S	A	L	U	N	E	C
R	S	S	A	C	C	R	P	F	P	H	E	G	A	C
E	T	S	U	C	P	L	O	T	C	R	N	G	L	I
B	T	N	O	S	T	A	R	S	C	Y	O	E	N	E
N	M	S	T	U	F	F	I	N	G	C	S	U	R	A
A	T	U	R	K	E	Y	O	P	L	N	A	G	T	R
R	S	D	E	C	O	R	A	T	I	O	N	S	W	S
C	E	E	R	T	S	A	M	T	S	I	R	H	C	S
S	T	H	G	I	L	S	G	N	I	K	C	O	T	S

CHRISTMASTIME

ANGEL
CARDS
CHRISTMAS TREE
CHURCH
CRANBERRY SAUCE
DECORATIONS
ELVES

FAMILY
GIFTS
LIGHTS
NOEL
PARTIES
PRESENTS
SANTA CLAUS

SNOW
SPROUTS
STARS
STOCKINGS
STUFFING
TINSEL
TURKEY

```
N N G E L S E N K I R C H E N
Z U N S T U T T G A R T F D H
W R H U D R E S D E N M R O A
L E I P Z I G E V A R I A B M
O M N O G N N O A E N N N E B
W B E U A G N C T E I R K R U
U E E B O A H S S C L L F H R
P R F L H E N S U S R E U A G
P G O R N U E L R U E I R U E
E C S E M E M D G R B K T S S
R H A G R E B L E D I E H E L
T S I D U S S E L D O R F N D
A D N U M T R O D M U N I C H
L A T D L E F E L E I B K U D
M W I E S B A D E N N O B H B
```

GERMAN CITIES

AACHEN	ESSEN	MUNICH
BERLIN	FRANKFURT	MUNSTER
BIELEFELD	GELSENKIRCHEN	NUREMBERG
BONN	HAMBURG	OBERHAUSEN
COLOGNE	HANOVER	STUTTGART
DORTMUND	HEIDELBERG	ULM
DRESDEN	KIEL	WIESBADEN
DUSSELDORF	LEIPZIG	WUPPERTAL

F	L	L	I	C	N	E	P	W	O	R	B	E	Y	E
A	D	B	R	E	K	O	H	L	P	E	N	C	I	L
L	F	L	E	P	S	E	N	O	Y	E	A	S	M	K
S	A	U	Y	E	E	E	D	R	N	P	R	A	S
E	C	S	E	Y	E	S	H	A	D	O	W	R	E	A
E	E	H	L	O	O	S	E	P	O	W	D	E	R	M
Y	P	E	I	A	A	O	L	E	K	S	A	S	C	E
E	O	R	N	L	I	I	G	L	L	L	F	I	E	C
L	W	D	E	L	P	U	P	I	I	A	E	E	C	A
A	D	Y	R	G	O	C	P	H	C	E	N	G	A	F
S	E	T	L	R	E	L	A	E	C	N	O	C	F	O
H	R	O	T	N	I	A	P	E	S	A	E	R	G	R
E	S	N	I	N	P	A	N	S	T	I	C	K	F	T
S	L	E	E	S	C	E	B	R	O	N	Z	E	R	F
I	R	R	S	K	F	C	R	E	S	N	A	E	L	C

COSMETICS

BLUSHER
BRONZER
CLEANSER
CONCEALER
EYEBROW PENCIL
EYELASH DYE
EYELINER

EYESHADOW
FACE CREAM
FACE MASK
FACE PACK
FACE POWDER
FALSE EYELASHES
GREASEPAINT

KOHL PENCIL
LIP GLOSS
LIP LINER
LOOSE POWDER
PANSTICK
ROUGE
TONER

I	P	L	B	A	I	M	I	L	U	B	R	G	S	L
A	N	A	V	M	E	A	S	L	E	S	W	N	A	M
I	E	S	S	T	Y	P	H	O	I	D	H	U	A	A
C	U	S	R	I	C	K	E	T	S	O	I	L	X	L
E	M	A	Y	Y	T	R	T	H	R	N	A	S	O	Z
P	O	F	R	S	A	I	T	C	F	R	S	R	P	H
O	N	E	Y	B	L	T	L	L	I	I	D	E	L	E
L	I	V	I	V	Y	A	U	A	S	B	I	M	L	I
A	A	E	S	P	R	E	P	O	H	E	A	R	A	M
A	S	R	H	R	N	U	B	S	H	P	B	A	M	E
N	M	U	C	Z	A	M	C	M	L	N	E	F	S	R
I	S	H	A	N	O	S	S	S	T	L	T	C	L	S
G	I	C	T	R	M	E	N	I	E	R	E	S	N	L
N	R	R	H	S	S	C	A	B	I	E	S	B	B	E
A	O	T	Z	M	A	S	T	O	I	D	I	T	I	S

DISEASES

ALOPECIA
ALZHEIMER'S
ANGINA
ASTHMA
BELL'S PALSY
BULIMIA
CROHN'S
DIABETES
ENCEPHALITIS

FARMER'S LUNG
INFLUENZA
LASSA FEVER
MALARIA
MASTOIDITIS
MEASLES
MENIERE'S
PNEUMONIA
RABIES

RICKETS
SARS
SCABIES
SCURVY
SMALLPOX
THROMBOSIS
TYPHOID
TYPHUS

N	M	L	R	P	A	C	G	N	I	K	N	I	H	T
I	G	N	E	C	A	P	U	T	L	L	M	O	P	C
G	P	U	I	A	N	U	L	L	R	E	B	C	C	U
G	N	T	U	P	N	N	G	U	N	S	L	R	C	S
O	E	L	D	O	O	N	O	T	K	O	O	B	A	K
N	G	D	G	N	M	E	A	U	N	W	S	N	L	R
N	S	C	S	A	M	L	L	O	N	N	N	U	B	M
N	N	C	O	D	P	L	U	U	U	C	B	S	R	E
E	M	O	D	O	A	S	K	O	R	A	B	C	L	M
N	C	N	W	I	A	N	O	A	T	R	R	P	E	B
L	C	E	C	D	N	N	E	R	U	A	N	T	T
E	R	O	U	N	A	I	M	G	E	S	I	A	I	N
S	O	B	E	I	U	D	L	M	W	R	N	C	H	N
L	N	M	R	M	R	N	C	E	R	E	B	R	U	M
A	E	E	G	C	L	E	C	R	R	N	I	O	R	I

USE YOUR HEAD

BRAIN
CAPUT
CEREBRUM
CRANIUM
CROWN

DOME
MENTAL POWERS
MIND
NOGGIN
NOODLE

NOUS
NUT
SKULL
THINKING CAP

E	Y	A	L	P	S	I	D	R	E	L	L	A	C	K
B	L	A	C	K	B	E	R	R	Y	S	R	P	G	E
T	H	I	R	D	G	E	N	E	R	A	T	I	O	N
M	S	M	A	R	T	P	H	O	N	E	C	R	A	E
D	D	U	A	L	B	A	N	D	P	H	O	N	E	E
E	I	T	S	P	E	A	K	E	R	P	H	O	N	E
N	E	F	S	O	I	A	D	E	H	T	H	A	G	N
O	H	A	R	M	R	I	G	A	E	P	V	O	E	W
H	A	G	S	M	O	D	N	N	R	O	F	P	A	A
P	R	H	T	R	E	D	R	A	I	A	P	P	I	A
O	E	S	D	D	S	E	C	P	O	M	N	S	M	S
E	M	N	S	F	T	S	D	N	A	B	I	R	T	U
D	A	O	R	N	P	V	O	I	C	E	M	A	I	L
I	C	E	I	G	H	T	O	O	T	E	U	L	B	L
V	E	N	O	H	P	E	T	I	L	L	E	T	A	S

PORTABLE PHONE

ANDROID
BLACKBERRY
BLUETOOTH
CALLER DISPLAY
CAMERA
CAR PHONE
DUAL-BAND PHONE
EDGE
GPRS

GPS
GSM
HANDS-FREE
INTERNET
IOS
RFID
SATELLITE PHONE
SMARTPHONE
SMS

SPEAKERPHONE
THIRD GENERATION
TRI-BAND
VIDEOPHONE
VOICEMAIL
VOIP
WAP

GEOGRAPHIC FEATURES

ARCHIPELAGO	GORGE	PLAIN
BAY	GRASSLAND	RIVERBED
BEACH	HILL	SEA
CANYON	ISLAND	STEPPE
CAVERN	JUNGLE	STREAM
CLIFF	LAKE	SWAMP
CREEK	MEADOW	TUNDRA
DESERT	MOUNTAIN	VALLEY
FOREST	OCEAN	VELD
GLACIER	PEAK	WATERFALL

ASSOCIATION FOOTBALL

```
K F D R C R D U G O U T E M P
C O T P R E M I E R S H I P R
I U H K C G T P U C D L R O W
K L E O W N G O A L L A F E U
D E A M K I N O I T A M R O F
A R D C I W H K O T O A I I E
E E H O T O F H I G R F N P
H F R I H C F R I D N E T I F
R E U P O S O L R T E D Y M F
E R A R I W E A A S D N M A O
V E N D I I C I E H L E M R K
O E E N S D P A S S O F U K C
R E D L E I F D I M G E D I I
W W P R O M O T I O N D F N K
L G R E K I R T S S O R C G E
```

CHIP	HALF-TIME	PROMOTION
CORNER	HEADER	RED CARD
CROSS	KICK-OFF	REFEREE
DEFENDER	MARKING	STRIKER
DUGOUT	MIDFIELDER	THROW-IN
DUMMY	OFFSIDE	UEFA
FIFA	OVERHEAD KICK	WINGER
FORMATION	OWN GOAL	WORLD CUP
FOUL	PASS	
GOLDEN GOAL	PREMIERSHIP	

```
U S F W I N D B R E A K W W C
W P K L B N S W I M M I N G S
B E E C I R E C L I N E R E K
E R A B O P N E L P N A A L L
A T B R B R P O S I W S B T S
C D A R I L S E H S H I B S E
H E R B E A E S R E G C W A S
B T C A R E N S L S S E E C S
A I N A U U Z L R K N C T D A
L K P E S G S E C R O R S N L
L G N I R R E B B U R E U A G
E B I K I N I F R E K A I S N
P U N W A V E S I N E M T A U
R T I U S M I W S L L S S S S
S K N U R T G N I H T A B S E
```

BEACH HOLIDAY

BATHING TRUNKS
BEACH BALL
BIKINI
BREEZE
FLIPPERS
ICE CREAM
KITE
LIFEGUARD

PARASOL
PEBBLES
RECLINER
ROCKS
RUBBER RING
SANDCASTLE
SEASHELLS
SNORKEL

SUNGLASSES
SUNSHINE
SWIMMING
SWIMSUIT
WAVES
WETSUIT
WINDBREAK

T	T	R	E	B	U	H	C	S	T	R	A	Z	O	M
N	T	A	L	L	I	S	I	B	E	L	I	U	S	D
I	L	L	E	C	R	U	P	U	E	H	W	E	N	R
D	I	Y	L	E	B	L	E	H	C	A	P	L	E	Y
R	S	R	K	B	S	S	T	A	G	V	S	G	A	B
E	Z	B	G	S	R	C	B	N	R	N	C	A	I	I
V	T	R	P	E	G	A	E	A	I	I	H	R	S	D
E	G	U	U	R	L	R	H	U	E	P	U	E	S	L
T	D	C	C	L	H	L	O	M	G	O	M	L	E	A
N	E	K	C	L	K	A	A	S	S	H	A	H	M	V
O	B	N	I	E	A	T	Y	C	S	C	N	A	O	I
M	U	E	N	D	R	T	T	D	T	U	N	M	S	V
L	S	R	I	N	O	I	M	A	N	T	M	Y	R	I
E	S	E	U	A	V	B	E	E	T	H	O	V	E	N
O	Y	P	R	H	D	S	S	S	U	A	R	T	S	E

FAMOUS COMPOSERS

ALLEGRI	GRIEG	PUCCINI
BACH	HANDEL	PURCELL
BEETHOVEN	HAYDN	SCARLATTI
BRAHMS	LISZT	SCHUBERT
BRUCKNER	MAHLER	SCHUMANN
BYRD	MESSIAEN	SIBELIUS
CHOPIN	MONTEVERDI	STRAUSS
DEBUSSY	MOZART	TALLIS
DVORAK	MUSSORGSKY	VIVALDI
ELGAR	PACHELBEL	WAGNER

R	Y	M	U	H	G	R	O	S	R	E	O	O	B	Y
D	T	S	S	A	R	G	S	A	P	M	A	P	E	A
O	A	H	C	M	T	I	M	O	T	H	Y	S	A	E
T	E	P	C	S	I	R	O	I	R	A	T	S	R	R
R	H	A	A	W	Y	B	Y	K	L	M	P	A	D	O
A	W	B	Y	P	M	E	P	E	A	L	W	R	G	B
P	K	F	T	A	Y	A	L	R	A	E	E	G	R	Y
S	C	E	B	A	D	R	R	R	G	M	B	T	A	Y
E	U	S	S	D	O	A	U	G	A	C	R	O	S	N
E	B	C	Y	Z	M	D	D	S	A	B	O	N	S	A
A	U	U	O	G	M	E	L	N	A	E	M	K	E	T
A	N	E	R	S	E	A	E	I	A	C	E	T	A	T
S	R	A	T	R	M	N	I	N	W	I	Y	N	M	A
T	S	A	Y	C	O	R	N	Z	A	R	A	E	A	R
S	O	K	S	M	W	A	C	C	E	Z	T	B	S	R

TYPES OF GRASS

BAMBOO
BARLEY
BEARD GRASS
BENT
BROME
BUCKWHEAT
CANE
CORN
ESPARTO

FESCUE
KNOTGRASS
MAIZE
MARRAM GRASS
MILLET
OATS
PADDY
PAMPAS GRASS
PAPYRUS

RATTAN
REED
RICE
RYE
SORGHUM
TIMOTHY
WILD OAT

M	A	F	A	V	I	T	U	P	E	R	A	T	E	T
N	S	D	E	R	H	S	O	T	R	A	E	T	R	N
H	E	T	A	O	G	A	E	V	A	H	F	A	A	A
N	R	H	S	M	S	B	T	A	C	O	S	T	N	P
M	U	I	L	L	S	T	O	E	H	T	O	E	N	
E	S	M	A	A	A	H	M	V	E	A	N	T	C	D
D	N	T	M	O	S	E	O	T	C	W	A	N	S	I
N	E	E	R	I	D	R	A	K	O	E	H	C	M	S
O	C	O	B	O	P	R	C	T	P	A	A	P	Y	P
C	O	B	W	P	G	I	O	I	M	R	U	R	D	A
R	U	N	A	I	P	T	N	M	I	G	C	K	P	R
R	O	S	N	T	O	S	E	F	N	E	E	N	R	A
N	I	E	I	G	O	R	Y	R	D	C	C	O	A	G
D	D	N	C	E	Z	I	C	I	T	I	R	C	C	E
N	S	L	E	T	A	G	I	T	S	A	C	K	O	S

PASSING THE BLAME

ATTACK
BLAME
CARP
CASTIGATE
CENSURE
COME DOWN ON
CONDEMN
CRITICIZE
DECRY
DENIGRATE

DISAPPROVE OF
DISPARAGE
GO TO TOWN ON
HAMMER
HAVE A GO AT
IMPUGN
KNOCK
NITPICK
PAN
ROAST

RUBBISH
SCARIFY
SLAM
SLATE
SNIPE AT
TEAR TO SHREDS
TRASH
VITUPERATE

SUPERFOODS

ACAI BERRIES
ALMONDS
AMARANTH
BEANS
BLUEBERRIES
BROCCOLI
CACAO
CHIA SEEDS
CRANBERRIES

EGGS
GINGER
GOJI BERRIES
GREEN TEA
KALE
KEFIR
LENTILS
MUSHROOMS
OATMEAL

PUMPKIN
QUINOA
SALMON
SEAWEED
SPINACH
SPIRULINA
WATERMELON

R	O	R	G	U	H	M	N	A	R	I	T	T	A	E
M	E	I	A	R	I	E	N	P	I	N	H	E	H	C
E	O	N	D	H	A	G	E	I	G	C	G	L	G	G
T	T	R	B	E	E	C	N	X	H	O	I	B	N	N
R	S	H	A	L	C	N	E	G	T	R	R	A	I	I
E	E	P	I	L	O	E	D	D	E	R	P	H	V	D
S	N	C	G	C	E	B	N	N	O	U	U	C	I	N
P	O	D	E	T	A	I	G	T	U	P	E	A	L	A
E	H	N	L	M	A	L	G	D	S	T	B	E	N	T
C	T	N	E	L	L	E	C	X	E	I	E	P	A	S
T	I	O	E	Y	H	T	R	O	W	B	G	M	E	P
A	E	X	E	M	P	L	A	R	Y	L	O	I	L	U
B	L	A	M	E	L	E	S	S	A	E	O	N	C	G
L	P	E	T	A	R	E	D	O	M	O	D	U	C	N
E	E	T	A	R	E	P	M	E	T	E	L	N	A	A

FEELING VIRTUOUS

ANGELIC
BLAMELESS
CLEAN-LIVING
DECENT
ETHICAL
EXCELLENT
EXEMPLARY

GOOD
GRACED
HONEST
INCORRUPTIBLE
INNOCENT
MODERATE
MORAL

RESPECTABLE
RIGHTEOUS
TEMPERATE
UNIMPEACHABLE
UPRIGHT
UPSTANDING
WORTHY

VEHICLES OF THE WORLD

BAROUCHE	MOTORBIKE	SULKY
BONESHAKER	PANTECHNICON	SURREY
BROUGHAM	PENNY-FARTHING	TANDEM
DRAY	PHAETON	TANK
GOLF CART	POST-CHAISE	TRACTOR
JINKER	PULLMAN	TRAP
JUGGERNAUT	RICKSHAW	TRICYCLE
LANDAU	SLEIGH	TROIKA
MAGLEV	SPACECRAFT	TROLLEYBUS

E	C	E	D	T	I	M	E	B	O	M	B	L	X	A
M	E	X	T	H	M	R	E	D	R	O	J	O	R	R
W	E	T	L	F	F	U	P	M	A	E	R	C	E	E
R	E	R	B	E	F	C	I	B	L	M	I	K	M	C
A	E	A	I	U	V	F	H	L	K	M	O	E	M	U
P	H	M	N	N	F	E	Y	A	T	H	E	D	A	A
P	C	O	F	I	G	F	L	I	R	D	T	C	H	S
E	T	V	T	I	R	U	C	O	H	M	I	A	P	G
D	I	E	R	O	S	K	E	A	D	R	M	N	O	N
C	W	S	G	P	E	H	E	F	I	L	I	D	P	I
A	S	M	R	T	O	F	F	E	E	R	L	Y	I	Y
N	E	P	M	A	R	M	A	L	A	D	E	N	L	L
D	E	E	R	E	T	S	O	O	B	O	M	Y	L	F
Y	R	T	N	E	I	D	E	R	G	N	I	I	O	A
E	F	F	Y	C	H	O	C	O	L	A	T	E	L	T

CANDY CRUSH SAGA

BOOSTER
CHARM
CHOCOLATE
CREAM PUFF
EXTRA MOVES
FISH
FLYING SAUCER
FREE SWITCH

INGREDIENT
JELLY FROG
LEVEL
LIFE
LOCKED CANDY
LOLLIPOP HAMMER
MARMALADE
MERINGUE

MR TOFFEE
ORDER
TICKET
TIFFI
TIME BOMB
TIME LIMIT
WRAPPED CANDY

T	S	O	H	G	O	M	A	T	L	A	N	T	I	S
R	E	T	S	N	O	M	S	S	E	N	H	C	O	L
L	S	A	S	U	D	E	M	N	D	R	A	G	O	N
A	N	B	I	G	F	O	O	T	T	R	E	A	L	A
D	O	G	D	O	G	T	D	I	A	M	R	E	M	L
Y	W	A	N	R	Y	R	I	A	F	T	I	H	L	L
O	M	E	E	O	I	S	A	N	H	R	P	S	O	A
F	A	D	R	A	G	S	A	U	E	A	M	E	R	H
T	I	N	A	M	T	M	R	R	C	A	A	M	M	L
H	D	N	H	F	N	T	E	H	C	Y	V	A	O	A
E	E	I	V	E	L	C	I	N	V	L	L	G	T	V
L	N	L	E	T	R	L	L	O	R	T	L	N	H
A	H	R	T	O	L	E	C	N	A	L	R	I	A	Y
K	G	E	S	E	O	I	C	A	R	U	S	G	H	H
E	H	M	S	D	O	Y	W	I	T	C	H	G	P	I

MYTHS AND LEGENDS

ACHILLES
ARTHUR
ASGARD
ATLANTIS
BIGFOOT
DRAGON
FAIRY
GHOST
GILGAMESH

GREEN MAN
ICARUS
LADY OF THE LAKE
LANCELOT
LOCH NESS MONSTER
MEDUSA
MERLIN
MERMAID
OGRE

PHANTOM
SNOW MAIDEN
SORCERER
TROLL
VALHALLA
VAMPIRE
WITCH

I	A	N	E	S	U	O	H	R	O	N	A	M	R	H
G	G	V	S	M	U	I	N	I	M	O	D	N	O	C
L	W	R	I	H	A	D	E	S	N	A	M	M	O	P
O	N	O	A	C	A	I	T	G	P	N	E	G	T	A
O	A	U	L	N	A	C	S	R	D	S	T	O	C	L
C	L	S	M	A	G	R	K	O	T	O	W	H	A	A
H	L	R	P	R	G	E	A	E	N	N	L	U	B	C
A	I	M	A	I	M	N	A	G	H	E	L	T	I	E
T	V	C	R	N	T	D	U	O	E	A	T	M	N	R
E	E	H	S	O	S	O	U	B	O	T	I	T	E	E
A	L	A	O	I	S	S	C	R	O	F	T	A	E	C
U	T	L	N	S	E	E	S	U	O	H	E	E	R	T
A	S	E	A	N	E	G	A	T	T	O	C	N	T	O
C	A	T	G	A	A	D	N	E	I	C	A	H	A	R
E	C	H	E	M	R	A	S	T	U	D	I	O	K	Y

SOMEWHERE TO LIVE

BUNGALOW
CABIN
CASTLE
CHALET
CHATEAU
CONDOMINIUM
COTTAGE
CROFT
GRANGE
HACIENDA

HOMESTEAD
HUT
IGLOO
LODGE
MAISONETTE
MANOR-HOUSE
MANSE
MANSION
MIA-MIA
PALACE

PARSONAGE
RANCH
RECTORY
SHACK
STUDIO
TOWN HOUSE
TREEHOUSE
VICARAGE
VILLA

E	L	S	L	M	E	C	I	D	Y	R	U	E	T	I
P	B	I	S	H	A	H	J	A	H	A	N	M	E	J
L	M	R	L	L	A	Y	L	A	E	S	M	U	O	Y
A	T	A	E	P	O	L	E	N	E	P	A	M	I	D
N	S	P	J	D	R	N	A	T	S	I	R	T	S	E
C	G	U	R	N	L	A	E	L	S	K	K	A	U	L
E	U	A	E	O	U	O	D	I	U	R	A	Z	E	I
L	I	N	T	S	N	N	S	H	M	I	N	M	H	L
O	N	S	E	A	S	T	Y	I	A	S	T	A	P	A
T	E	H	N	L	H	Y	E	O	R	H	O	H	R	H
O	V	A	O	I	E	E	D	P	Y	N	N	A	O	O
C	E	H	S	E	T	H	R	O	P	A	Y	L	M	H
S	R	B	M	O	O	L	J	U	L	I	E	T	E	C
J	E	N	A	R	C	I	S	S	U	S	H	R	O	E
E	O	Y	S	V	C	C	L	E	O	P	A	T	R	A

FAMOUS LOVERS

CLEOPATRA
DELILAH
ECHO
EURYDICE
GUINEVERE
HELEN
ISOLDE
JULIET
KRISHNA

LANCELOT
LAYLA
MAJNUN
MARK ANTONY
MUMTAZ MAHAL
NARCISSUS
ODYSSEUS
ORPHEUS
PARIS

PENELOPE
PYRAMUS
RADHA
ROMEO
SAMSON
SHAH JAHAN
THISBE
TRISTAN

```
G N I C N A D A P K G A T F W
P M U S I C A L R A A A R I O
N O I T I B I H X E I E E R H
W C U S L I Q M S S P O C E S
U E S O S G G U C R K O N W T
I K A N A E N S I M N Q O O E
C O M E D Y I I T A A U C R P
I A H P R T K C A G A I S K P
R R T R E E S H B I P Z G S U
C A E I C R U A O C A A A I P
U K E U I A B L R S C N R O G
S Y P U T B S L E H P O O T S
L C A I A A R R A O W O E G Y
K I T L L C S S R W I A R U C
G A M E P R M R O D E O E T A
```

PUBLIC ENTERTAINMENT

AEROBATICS	FIREWORKS	PARTY
BUSKING	GAME	PLAY
CABARET	GIG	PUPPET SHOW
CIRCUS	KARAOKE	QUIZ
COMEDY	MAGIC SHOW	RECITAL
CONCERT	MUSICAL	RODEO
DANCING	MUSIC HALL	SPORT
EXHIBITION	OPERA	

E	T	A	M	S	O	F	O	R	M	A	T	E	E	T
I	E	M	U	I	S	E	N	G	A	M	R	E	T	B
E	T	A	T	C	A	L	E	E	L	M	H	T	A	B
P	E	T	A	N	I	G	L	A	O	I	E	A	R	I
R	O	T	I	O	D	I	D	E	N	C	T	R	D	C
U	E	T	I	B	M	U	L	P	A	R	A	U	Y	A
E	R	T	A	N	N	A	T	E	T	O	N	E	H	R
X	T	A	A	S	A	Y	M	T	E	C	I	T	O	B
N	A	A	N	S	G	T	A	B	O	M	A	N	O
A	R	R	E	I	I	I	N	L	I	S	U	H	O	N
Z	N	O	O	L	N	S	U	A	B	M	L	P	M	A
I	P	T	C	B	O	E	E	M	M	I	A	L	N	T
D	E	G	L	A	U	B	E	R	O	C	K	U	E	E
E	E	T	A	L	Y	X	O	B	R	A	C	S	R	Y
L	I	T	H	A	T	E	E	D	I	M	O	R	B	M

SALTS

ALGINATE	IODIDE	OSMATE
ALUMINATE	LACTATE	PLUMBITE
AZIDE	LITHATE	POTASSIUM
BICARBONATE	MAGNESIUM	RESINATE
BORAX	MALATE	ROCK
BROMIDE	MALONATE	SULPHATE
CARBOXYLATE	MANGANITE	TANNATE
CORN	MICROCOSMIC	URANINE
FORMATE	MONOHYDRATE	URATE
GLAUBER	OLEATE	

S	U	O	A	E	Z	Z	A	M	U	N	D	S	E	N
D	E	C	K	A	N	N	F	S	C	O	T	T	S	V
N	I	A	I	A	O	I	O	A	M	A	I	H	A	F
I	R	D	M	N	E	B	B	S	N	C	A	O	M	L
D	M	S	N	N	B	C	L	L	S	C	O	N	R	I
N	A	M	N	G	L	O	E	A	K	K	O	O	P	N
T	H	E	E	O	Y	Y	L	L	B	S	I	R	K	D
Z	S	N	K	M	I	K	E	O	D	I	N	R	O	E
R	H	D	R	E	S	T	N	U	P	O	S	F	E	R
A	T	O	U	S	O	I	H	N	E	S	N	A	N	S
L	O	Z	B	N	F	N	A	L	L	E	G	A	M	A
E	B	A	N	F	F	C	O	U	S	T	E	A	U	O
I	A	M	A	G	A	D	S	U	B	M	U	L	O	C
G	C	B	E	Y	R	A	L	L	I	H	M	O	R	G
H	H	E	N	S	O	N	V	E	S	P	U	C	C	I

GREAT EXPLORERS

AMUNDSEN
BAFFIN
BALBOA
BLY
BURKE
CABOT
COLUMBUS
COOK
COUSTEAU
DA GAMA

DIAZ
DRAKE
ERIKSSON
FIENNES
FLINDERS
GOMES
HENSON
HILLARY
HUDSON
MAGELLAN

MENDOZA
NANSEN
POLO
RALEIGH
SCOTT
SHACKLETON
STANLEY
TASMAN
VESPUCCI

```
Y E K A T E R I N B U R G E O
G T S T K R A S N O Y A R S K
N K M N O D N O V O T S O R K
K E O K S R I B I S O V O N T
H M T G R U B N E R O O P T Y
A E A V O U A T A N K T O O U
B R A D O N S A R K R A S L M
A O V R U L M K V S Y R Z Y E
R V A N S F G O S A M A R A N
O O B A E S A O S V M S A T N
V O R O N E Z H G C E R S T L
S I I R K U T S K R O H E I O
K Y A R O S L A V L A W Z P O
K L U A N R A B A D S D U I Z
M M A K H A C H K A L A O K A
```

RUSSIAN CITIES

BARNAUL
IRKUTSK
IZHEVSK
KAZAN
KEMEROVO
KHABAROVSK
KRASNODAR
KRASNOYARSK

MAKHACHKALA
MOSCOW
NOVOSIBIRSK
ORENBURG
PERM
ROSTOV-ON-DON
SAMARA
SARATOV

TOLYATTI
TOMSK
TYUMEN
UFA
VOLGOGRAD
VORONEZH
YAROSLAVL
YEKATERINBURG

S	O	U	B	A	S	E	B	A	L	L	L	A	P	A
C	S	E	L	B	U	O	D	S	I	N	N	E	T	B
S	O	O	B	A	E	Y	R	S	B	N	H	G	B	E
A	W	S	O	C	C	E	R	A	R	E	L	A	Y	S
L	A	A	L	I	E	C	S	G	N	I	L	R	U	C
B	T	E	N	E	L	K	U	B	C	L	U	I	O	S
A	E	L	A	H	E	H	E	N	A	I	G	C	S	O
L	R	E	L	T	A	S	T	B	C	N	E	E	A	N
L	P	B	B	A	S	N	Y	E	I	N	I	H	I	E
R	O	A	E	O	B	E	D	L	I	S	A	O	L	K
L	L	W	R	T	L	T	C	B	L	G	L	C	I	B
L	O	C	A	L	W	Y	F	N	A	B	L	K	N	L
L	A	P	O	M	C	L	I	O	N	L	L	E	G	R
L	S	V	G	N	I	W	O	R	S	Y	L	Y	E	N
E	E	B	S	I	R	F	E	T	A	M	I	T	L	U

TEAM SPORTS

BASEBALL
BASKETBALL
CURLING
CYCLING
HANDBALL
ICE HOCKEY

LACROSSE
RELAY
ROWING
SAILING
SOCCER
SOFTBALL

TENNIS DOUBLES
ULTIMATE FRISBEE
VOLLEYBALL
WATER POLO

SOLUTIONS ⓩ

Over 200 puzzles

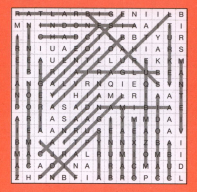

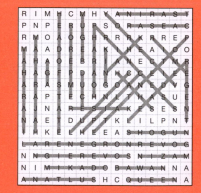

Page 7

Page 10

Page 8

Page 11

Page 9

Page 12

Page 13

Page 16

Page 14

Page 17

Page 15

Page 18

Page 25

Page 28

Page 26

Page 29

Page 27

Page 30

Page 31

Page 32

Page 33

Page 34

Page 35

Page 36

Page 37

Page 40

Page 38

Page 41

Page 39

Page 42

Page 43

Page 46

Page 44

Page 47

Page 45

Page 48

Page 49

Page 50

Page 51

Page 52

Page 53

Page 54

Page 55

Page 58

Page 56

Page 59

Page 57

Page 60

Page 61

Page 64

Page 62

Page 65

Page 63

Page 66

228

Page 67

Page 70

Page 68

Page 71

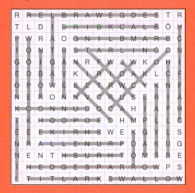

Page 69

Page 72

Page 73

Page 76

Page 74

Page 77

Page 75

Page 78

Page 79

Page 80

Page 81

Page 82

Page 83

Page 84

Page 85

```
K N E B U T U A L U T A P S E
B S I N E R O T A C C I S E D
R U A B P A T R E D N I L Y C
E T N L E C K S S L I D E D K
B R F S F L R E T T I N R R S
U I I H E C L U R I A C L O A
T P L S V N I J C A R N E P L
G O T I A E B R A I R D P F
N D E D L T E U T R B R E E R
T R I C T E B R E E L O R E
L R P R O E L E C N M N E M T
I O A T T R T I L R E U S I L
O T P E U U S C A S M R L R I
B E E P A B E T M R A R I O F
T R R G I R P I P E T T E E V
```

Page 86

```
A G E E D I S Y R T N U O C C
H N K P U B S N T Y P I E R S
O I C S L S O I L B E I K E
I S G O L E N R E A S G E E L
N S S H C I P A K L E U H T
O O G E L N D R L N I N O R S
S T I B S A S O E C E A U V A
N R A R R T N N F C C Y V O C
A E N I E R S D O F H C S N M
K B D D V A E S W A A E A D
E A U E O T G U I T D D U R E
S C B S L H G R D R I O U N C
P S H E C S A O U D P I N O S
C E L T I C H S R E D H A R
C E I S M R A F E S T L I K A
```

Page 87

```
V N S E C H E N I N B L A N C
I E R R E C N A S L E V A T C
N A S V M U S C A D E T E A
H D Y O B E A U J O L A I S V
O J L L P M E V O U V R A Y A
V E V E R B D M T C K A Y B
E R A D E E L E T A C S U M
R E N T S V B T O O M A K S D
D P E N P A S S E A L C A A
E I R A O O U E D I A I O L G
A G O M B R S U C K O N C H A
S O R E T T C E I T V A E E L
T N U R E C A N A R Y N A C A
W O C R F R A S C A T I U M
L E D O R V I E T O G T O B T
```

Page 88

```
N O T T U M W S R E T T O R F
S A F K E S S N O E G I P B T
O I R S L R E G R U B M A H E
A O O I R G R R R E L B A L
P O E S T E A K G A H T C K
G R O U S E A U K B E A U I C
S A U S A G E E Q B A T R B U
B N O S I N E V A I R X K R N
E B A C O N E L N T T O E A K
L K M L E K T O N G U E Y W S
O I R A O C E R A H L P N G
S D N A G M A U T B N I A O
S N C G T R B R D D E V T R P
I E E T N A S A E H P E O A
R Y S C H I C K E N R R F A E
```

Page 89

```
P O E F S E P O N I A R D S A
I Q B A Y O N E T R A E P S L
K U Q E E K S P R A O S S E E
E A K W A H A M O T C N F T Y
C R E G G A D O T I L A W P
F T N D W A D E M A N E P E E
A E S R M R L I I K R O D E W
P R G O A T R E I P A R B E
O S L W T A E I C L I O F P T
R T A S R O W G A G M D A E E
T A I D O O K R U Y E G Y C H
L F V A B L R R A O N R P N C
A F E O N O T L A V E E A A
C I L R W A C K P D U F W L M
R L L B V E F I N K K C I L F
```

Page 90

```
R T I G E O G R A P H Y A G H
Y I M L Y Y G O L O I B G E O
A R Y G O L O E G C S S N O M
E Y O H O I H S E A O P E M E
M R B T S Y A G B L C H N E E
A T U E S E I R C I Y G T C
T S I T L I N M A U A S L R O
H I C C A O H A Y L L I I V N
E M O L N R G H P U S C S S O
M E H B G Y E Y T S T S H M M
A H T O U M D T M E U I U M I
T C L T A G R C T D S H E C
I A A A G C A I O L I C Y B S
C R E N E E M G A C E G G G N
S T H Y S T A L M Y S A C L S
```

Page 91

Page 94

Page 92

Page 95

Page 93

Page 96

Page 97

Page 100

Page 98

Page 101

Page 99

Page 102

Page 103

Page 106

Page 104

Page 107

Page 105

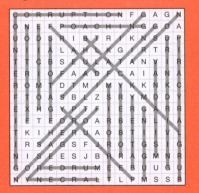

Page 108

Page 109

Page 110

Page 111

Page 112

Page 113

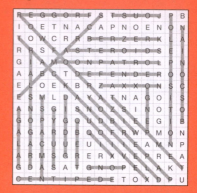

Page 114

Page 115

Page 118

Page 116

Page 119

Page 117

Page 120

Page 121

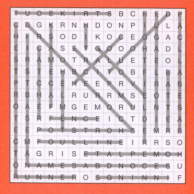

Page 124

Page 122

Page 125

Page 123

Page 126

Page 127

Page 128

Page 129

Page 130

Page 131

Page 132

Page 133

Page 134

Page 135

Page 136

Page 137

Page 138

Page 145

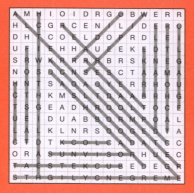

Page 146

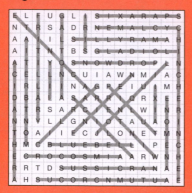

Page 147

Page 148

Page 149

Page 150

Page 151

Page 152

Page 153

Page 154

Page 155

Page 156

Page 157

Page 160

Page 158

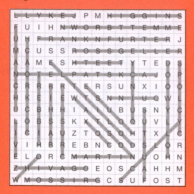

Page 161

Page 159

Page 162

Page 163

Page 166

Page 164

Page 167

Page 165

Page 168

Page 169

Page 170

Page 171

Page 172

Page 173

Page 174

Page 175

Page 178

Page 176

Page 179

Page 177

Page 180

Page 181

Page 184

Page 182

Page 185

Page 183

Page 186

Page 187

Page 190

Page 188

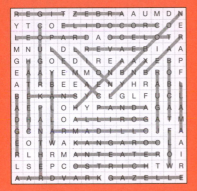

Page 191

Page 189

Page 192

Page 193

Page 196

Page 194

Page 197

Page 195

Page 198

Page 199

Page 200

Page 201

Page 202

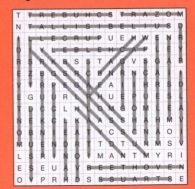

Page 203

Page 204

Page 205

Page 208

Page 206

Page 209

Page 207

Page 210